W9-CGY-371

Introductory
Statistical Mechanics for
Physicists

BOOKS BY D. K. C. MACDONALD

Introductory Statistical Mechanics for Physicists
Principles of Thermoelectricity
Noise and Fluctuations: An Introduction

Introductory Statistical Mechanics for Physicists

D. K. C. MacDonald
Division of Pure Physics
National Research Council, Ottawa, Canada

John Wiley & Sons, Inc., New York · London · Sydney

THIRD PRINTING, SEPTEMBER, 1965

Library of Congress Catalog Card Number: 63-11441

Printed in the United States of America

SECOND PRINTING, FEBRUARY, 1964

PREFACE

Statistical mechanics is, I think, frequently regarded by graduating physicists as a rather difficult and even esoteric subject. It is true that strict and critical establishment of the fundamentals must be considered a very specialized discipline, and undoubtedly the application of statistical mechanics to many complex problems demands advanced and ingenious techniques. However, for a wide range of physicists there seems no reason why statistical mechanics should not be a very useful and familiar tool. I do not pretend to be in any way a real specialist in the subject; but I feel that I have had the advantage of using elementary statistical mechanics, mainly through early interests in problems of Brownian Movement and fluctuations, before perhaps I even *knew* I was using statistical mechanics! It may be that, had I known at that time of the awe which often seems to surround statistical mechanics, I would never have dared to become involved.

Recently I have been teaching an introductory course on statistical mechanics to undergraduate physicists at the University of Ottawa, and I owe a sincere debt to my colleague, Dr. J. S. Dugdale, (who previously taught that course) for leading me to *Introduction to Statistical Mechanics* by Rushbrooke (1949). To me this seems a most admirable book as a whole; my main justification for attempting to write the present book is that Rushbrooke's work is intended, in his own words: "for students . . . of limited mathematical experience . . . especially in the field of physical chemistry," whereas I have felt that I would like to write a considerably shorter monograph which might be of help primarily to those reading for a degree in physics.

At best, this book can only hope to be a modest introduction to such classic texts as those of Fowler (1936), Fowler and Guggenheim (1939), and Tolman (1938). The primary aim is to give physicists some initial confidence in *using* statistical mechanics, and perhaps also some "feel" for the breadth and power of the subject. I have tried therefore to present the physical essentials simply (often following Rushbrooke's lead) and at the same time I hope, fairly, and with an indication of critical questions of interest to physicists. Thus some remarks are made in Appendix II on the move from the calculation of the entropy of an assembly at strictly constant energy (essentially the so-called "micro-canonical ensemble") to the direct calculation of the Helmholtz free energy at a given temperature (introducing the "canonical ensemble"); however, in the text itself the transition is deliberately made almost without comment.

My own experience, such as it is, in the field as a physicist has never led me personally to use the "grand canonical ensemble" or the corresponding "grand partition function." Apart from my own mental laziness, this is perhaps because that technique often becomes really profitable when one has to do vitally with open systems, which tend to lie outside the immediate province of physics. I offer this as some justification, together with the avowedly introductory character of this book, for making only passing reference to the "grand canonical ensemble" and "grand partition function."

I am grateful to Mrs. T. F. Armitage and Miss I. Assing for typing the various drafts of the manuscript, and also to Mrs. A. Cuccaro for further assistance. I wish to thank warmly Dr. J. S. Dugdale for many discussions and very pleasant collaboration on problems of statistical mechanics, and to thank Drs. T. H. K. Barron and A. M. Guénault for reading the manuscript and for assistance with the proofs. I am also grateful to my wife, Moira, and daughter, Aileen, for help in correcting the proofs and to the staff of Messers. John Wiley and Sons, Inc., for their unfailing courtesy.

D. K. C. MacDonald

January, 1963

CONTENTS

1

BASIC PRINCIPLES

1.1 INTRODUCTION

1.1.1 THE ROLE OF THERMODYNAMICS

It is quite customary to restrict the name thermodynamics to the study of physical systems which are in equilibrium. From this standpoint, thermodynamics, strictly speaking, does not concern itself with how, or at what rate, systems reach over-all thermal equilibrium but assumes that we can *recognize* such a state when it is achieved, and thermodynamics then tells us essentially how to relate one thermodynamic quantity to another. It is of course true that the greatest achievement of classical thermodynamics, namely the Second Law, essentially points out that in so-called natural, irreversible processes the entropy S in a closed system always tends to increase. But on the other hand classical thermodynamics deals with this question only by evaluating the entropy in the final and initial states, both treated as being in *thermodynamic equilibrium*, and says nothing about how the increase of entropy occurs during the irreversible transition from the initial to the final state.

In more recent years there have been developments, linked particularly with such names as Onsager (1931), de Donder, de Groot (1951), and Prigogine (1947), aimed at extending the sort of techniques used in classical thermodynamics so that they may be applied to irreversible processes themselves, such as the continuous flow of a gas from a region of high pressure to one of lower pressure, or the flow of electric current in a conductor with resistance in it. This extension of thermodynamic ideas is usually known as "irreversible thermodynamics," and the term "classical thermodynamics" is to be thought of, in that context, as being in contrast to irreversible thermodynamics.* Broadly speaking, the term thermodynamics without modification is often taken to mean the thermodynamics of systems in equilibrium, and we shall follow that practice here.

The significance of thermodynamics is that, strictly speaking, we refuse to delve into the supposed "microscopic,"† or better atomic, behavior of the system we are looking at. The whole technique of classical thermodynamics, and its power and corresponding weakness, is that we try to characterize the behavior of the system with which we are dealing by a few *macroscopic* variables, such as pressure, volume, electric field, or magnetic field, and then try to predict as much of its behavior as we can in terms of these variables using the basic Laws of Thermodynamics. This limitation to a few macroscopic variables means that thermodynamic predictions about the behavior of the system are of considerable generality and should *not* depend on any particular molecular hypothesis we may have about the structure of the system on the "microscopic" level. And, by the same token, thermodynamics of itself cannot in general distinguish between the validity of one proposed molecular model and that of another.

Thus, for example, thermodynamics of itself cannot say whether $pV = RT$ is more correct as an equation of state for a mole of a particular gas than, say, $pV + a/V = RT$. However, it can tell us, irrespective of any particular molecular hypothesis we may make, whether there are inconsistencies in our assumptions when we, as physicist, engineer, or chemist, have specified that a system has some particular equation of state. Thus classical thermodynamics can show us that a molar internal energy‡ $E = 3RT/2$ is inconsistent with an equation of state $pV + a/V = RT$, or that the equation of state $pV = RT$ is inconsistent with an internal energy $E = (3RT/2)(1 + c/V)$.

I have always felt that one of the most striking examples of the power of classical thermodynamics was at the hands of William Thom-

* It has been argued that classical thermodynamics should rather be known as "thermostatics," and irreversible thermodynamics more simply as "thermodynamics." An alternative choice might be "equilibrium thermodynamics" and "nonequilibrium thermodynamics."

† This adjective is used throughout as being in contrast to "macroscopic" and refers specifically to behavior on the atomic, or molecular, level. It does *not* of course imply any direct connection with an optical microscope.

‡ The symbol U is also used frequently for (internal) energy in thermodynamics, but we prefer to use E here for the energy since it is identical with the total energy of the system which we shall encounter in statistical mechanics and which is usually denoted by E.

son (Lord Kelvin) (1854) when he was dealing with thermoelectricity. Actually it required some courage to apply classical thermodynamics to thermoelectricity, since the whole situation is complicated by the inevitable presence of *irreversible* electrical and thermal resistance. If these worries can be overlooked, however, the thermoelectric phenomena *themselves* may be treated as reversible (i.e., as essentially equilibrium phenomena); Kelvin then argued that there should be a thermodynamic connection between the two thermoelectric parameters, namely the Peltier heat Π and the (Seebeck) thermoelectric power $\mathcal{S}$ which at that time were the two well-known thermoelectric phenomena. If we consider a thermoelectric circuit of two conducting materials, 1 and 2, and assume that Π and $\mathcal{S}$ are sufficient as macroscopic parameters to describe the thermoelectric behavior, *but make no additional "microscopic" or molecular hypothesis about how thermoelectricity arises,* we can show, as Thomson did, that

$$\mathcal{S}_{12} = \frac{d\Pi_{12}}{dT} = \frac{\Pi_{12}}{T} \qquad \textbf{ERRONEOUS!}$$

Thomson tested his prediction on experimental data and found that it was not valid. He then had the great courage, and confidence in his thermodynamic arguments, to conclude that the macroscopic description in terms only of Peltier heat and Seebeck potential must be inadequate; consequently he predicted that a further macroscopic thermoelectric effect must necessarily exist. This is what we know today as the Thomson Heat, and Thomson himself subsequently verified through experiment the existence of this important additional macroscopic thermoelectric parameter. Thus thermodynamics itself can sometimes point out to us inconsistencies and inadequacies in our macroscopic description of a system, and moreover indicate the way to correcting this defect.

Very often thermodynamics itself can also help us to determine one macroscopic parameter from a knowledge of others that we have already measured. So, for example, we have the well-known relation between specific heats at constant pressure and constant volume, namely

$$C_p - C_V = -T\left(\frac{\partial p}{\partial V}\right)_T \left(\frac{\partial V}{\partial T}\right)_p^2. \tag{1}$$

For a solid or a liquid it is generally much easier to *measure* C_p than C_V; on the other hand, in setting up some more or less fundamental physical theory about the basic structure of a solid or fluid, it is usually much easier to predict C_V *theoretically*. Equation 1 may then enable us to determine C_V for this theoretical comparison from experimental data which we already have about C_p for a particular substance, together with other available experimental data. We must emphasize again that these achievements of classical thermodynamics are independent of any specific assumptions we may make about the *molecular* behavior of any particular system being considered.

1.1.2 The Aim of Statistical Mechanics

It would be ridiculous to pretend today, however, that we do not have many ideas, concepts, and theories about the molecular and atomic structure of matter, which prove of the greatest value in understanding the behavior of matter around us,* and we are naturally very anxious to link together in as general a manner as possible our molecular hypotheses and models with our macroscopic observations. This sort of "bridge building" has of course been going on for a long time, and ter Haar (1954) points out that the interpretation of the "perfect gas law" in terms of molecular ideas is a very old one. The aim of statistical mechanics, regarded strictly, is to give a unified and established method for predicting macroscopic thermodynamic (equilibrium) parameters, such as the internal energy, the equilibrium pressure, the magnetic susceptibility, or the specific heat, of a substance from appropriate models that we may propose for the *molecular* behavior of the substance.

The name statistical mechanics arises because we think of the job of mechanics (either Newtonian mechanics or wave mechanics) as that of predicting how individual particles, or "elements," will behave, but in order to relate these directly to the behavior of matter *in bulk*, it is not surprising that we must use *statistical* methods. Perhaps the main thing to bear in mind is that, roughly speaking, even as small a piece as one-thousandth of a cubic millimeter of a typical solid will contain something like 10^{16} to 10^{17} atoms. This is an enormous number which should be adequate to give very great confidence to statistical predictions.† In visualizing the magnitude of this number it

* It is an odd tragedy that we are told (cf. Broda, 1955) that Boltzmann's suicide on September 5, 1906 was caused to some degree by depression arising from opposition by workers such as Mach and Ostwald to the atomic theory of matter, to which of course Boltzmann contributed so much understanding.

† Consider a simple example. We have some number N of supposedly independent "elements" (e.g., human voters, motor vehicles), each of which makes some simple choice (to wear brown or gray gloves, or to take the left or right fork at a road junction). Then the typical variation, or fluctuation, in numbers making

may help to recall that it would probably suffice to give every man, woman, and child who has ever lived on this earth about a million atoms each.

Thus we must seek some general and convenient bridge to take us from some "microscopic," or molecular, description of a body to some macroscopic, thermodynamic parameter which can be measured in bulk. In line with our earlier remarks about classical thermodynamics, we should say that statistical mechanics is normally taken to mean this bridge from a "microscopic" description to the *equilibrium* macroscopic thermodynamic description. Much work goes on, nonetheless, to try to extend statistical mechanics so that *non*equilibrium situations may be dealt with, work very closely akin to the extension of classical thermodynamics to irreversible processes and so leading to so-called "irreversible thermodynamics." In this short monograph we discuss primarily the basic role of statistical mechanics, that of treating equilibrium situations, in which the theory is well established. More particularly, we shall concern ourselves on the one hand with the analysis of more or less perfectly crystalline solids and related models and on the other hand with more or less ideal gas models, because in these situations the theory is well established, and moreover because they are of great importance to physicists.

Apart from some discussion of liquid He^3 and He^4 as idealized Fermi-Dirac and Bose-Einstein "gases," we shall not attempt to deal with liquids. At the end of the last chapter we shall try to indicate very briefly some of the basic questions that arise in attempting to understand, and deal with, irreversible processes in relation to statistical mechanics.

1.2 THE BOLTZMANN-PLANCK EQUATION

1.2.1 The Foundations by Boltzmann

The kinetic theory of gases* was developed in the last century particularly by James Clerk Maxwell and Ludwig Boltzmann, and Boltzmann in 1872 presented his so-called H-theorem. Boltzmann showed

---

the choice, as we examine successive groups of N "elements," will be about $\sqrt{N}$. In other words, the *relative* fluctuation in any given group is about $\sqrt{N}/N = 1/\sqrt{N}$. Hence if $N \sim 10^{16}$, the typical relative fluctuation to be found from group to group of N elements will only be about 10^{-8}, a satisfyingly small number.

* The name of Waterston (1846, 1892) is much less well known, but he also did pioneer work in the kinetic theory of gases.

that the entropy S of a gas could be related directly to a certain integral (say $\tilde{H}$) over the distribution function, $f(v_x, v_y, v_z)$, of the gas molecules. In thermodynamic equilibrium it is well known that the Maxwell-Boltzmann distribution function involves the energy of gas molecules and the absolute temperature T, and so the *possibility* of making this identification with a thermodynamic parameter (namely the entropy S) is perhaps not too surprising. With certain apparently reasonable assumptions, Boltzmann showed analytically that this $\tilde{H}$-function would always increase with time* toward a certain maximum value, as the state of a gas evolved toward equilibrium from some initial distribution, say $f(0)$ at time $t = 0$; in turn, this increasing $\tilde{H}$, governed by $f(t)$ at any time t, could then be understood as an increasing probability for the gas system to be in the particular configuration $f(t)$. This interpretation of the $\tilde{H}$-function in terms of probability may also seem not too surprising if we bear in mind that the distribution function f is itself essentially a generalized probability for finding a gas molecule with some particular velocity (and with particular space coordinates if these are included in the distribution function). Ultimately, then, Boltzmann established a close relation between the thermodynamic entropy S and the relative probability for the gas to be in that particular state.

1.2.2 The Planck Generalization

Planck took a further decisive step forward when he generalized the Boltzmann relationship to *all* thermodynamic systems, and moreover made the relationship quantitatively precise. In principle Planck reduced the problem to a pure matter of *counting* the number of distinguishable atomic, or molecular "microscopic," configurations, say Ω, that the system could have consistent with the required *macroscopic* thermodynamic state. It was necessary to wait for Planck to take this final step since, until the idea of separate quantum states had in effect been introduced through Planck's quantum hypothesis, no precise count of such "microscopic states" could really be made in classi-

* More correctly, it should be said that Boltzmann defined

$$H = \iiint f \ln f \, dv_x \, dv_y \, dv_z,$$

and this function H then always *diminishes* with time. Thus we may say, for consistency, that "our" $\tilde{H} = -H$, so that indeed $\tilde{H}$ will always increase with time. (Actually Boltzmann (1872) *originally* used the symbol E for these integrals, but his work is always referred to today as the "H-theorem.")

cal mechanics.* Planck argued that we can generalize the Boltzmann relation between entropy and probability to read simply and directly

$$\boxed{S = k \ln \Omega}, \tag{2}$$

where, we repeat, Ω is the number of distinguishable "microscopic" configurations of the system under discussion, consistent with the macroscopic state characterized by the thermodynamic entropy S. The constant k is what we know today as Boltzmann's constant ($k = 1.4 \times 10^{-16}$ erg/deg), but it might well be called the Boltzmann-Planck constant. Correspondingly, we would refer to Eq. 2 as the *Boltzmann-Planck equation.*

1.2.3 Planck's Analysis

If we accept, as Planck did following Boltzmann's initial lead, that it *should* be possible to relate directly the thermodynamic entropy S purely to the number of permissible microscopic configurations, it is straightforward to show that a relation of the form of Eq. 2 must indeed hold. Starting from the proposition that we may write

$$S = f(\Omega), \tag{3}$$

where f is a universal function of a single variable Ω, Planck (*loc. cit.*) considers how " . . . in the case of two mutually independent systems (1) and (2), the entropy on the one hand, and the statistical weight of the total system (1,2) on the other, are built up from the properties of the individual systems." Since the two systems are independent, we may add their entropies; i.e.,

$$S_{12} = S_1 + S_2, \tag{4}$$

* We quote directly from Planck (1932, p. 226): " . . . we shall immediately express the hypothesis in its most definite and most far-reaching form, a form which goes considerably beyond the classical theory and has shown itself to be superior in competition with it. It runs: . . . '*Every macroscopic state of a physical system comprises a perfectly definite number of microscopic states of the system, and this number represents the thermodynamic probability or the statistical weight* [Ω] *of the macroscopic state.*' It is a measure of the entropy S of the system in the corresponding macroscopic state, thus:

$$S = f(\Omega)$$

where f denotes a universal function of a single argument."

and "since every microscopic state of the one system can be combined with every microscopic state of the other system,"

$$\Omega_{12} = \Omega_1 \cdot \Omega_2 \tag{5}$$

Thus

$$f(\Omega_1\Omega_2) = f(\Omega_1) + f(\Omega_2), \tag{6}$$

and the general solution of Eq. 6 is to write

$$f(\Omega) = \bar{k} \ln \Omega, \tag{7}$$

or

$$S = k \ln \Omega, \qquad \text{i.e., Eq. 2}$$

assuming that we may identify the constant $\bar{k}$ as the familiar Boltzmann's constant k. Planck points out that

> "The logarithmic relationship between entropy and probability was first disclosed by L. Boltzmann. But the equation [our Eq. 2] differs in two essential points from that of Boltzmann.
>
> Firstly the universal factor, k, is missing in Boltzmann's expression; . . . . Secondly, and this is a much more significant point, in Boltzmann's classical statistics a factor of proportionality remains completely indefinite in the value of [Ω] . . . this causes the value of the entropy to contain an undetermined additive constant. For Boltzmann regarded the counting up of the microscopic states belonging to a definite macroscopic state only as an arithmetical device of a certain arbitrary character . . . . In contrast with this the value of the entropy [in Eq. 2 due to Planck] has . . . a perfectly definite, absolute, and, indeed positive, value."

The Boltzmann-Planck equation (Eq. 2) thus in principle gives the foundation for statistical mechanics; our problem then is to evaluate the number of complexions or distinguishable microscopic states Ω. As Planck himself says, " . . . the fundamental relation [Eq. 2] furnishes a method of expressing the whole thermodynamic behavior of a system in terms of its microscopic structure, [but] we have not yet, of course, solved the problem by merely establishing the relation. For we have yet to calculate the number [Ω] for any case that may present itself; this problem has been solved completely for only a few systems of simple type." A present-day expert in statistical mechanics would feel that we had by now learned to solve the problem of calculating Ω for much more than "a few systems of simple type," but we shall essentially follow Planck here by restricting our attention to the relatively straightforward applications of equilibrium statistical mechanics to nearly perfectly crystalline solids on the one hand and to the almost "ideal gas" situation of noninteracting, freely moving "particles" on the other. Nevertheless, even this latter idealized model will enable us to look at such problems as conduction electrons in a metal, electromagnetic radiation treated as "photons," and, following the bold arguments of F. London (1938), the behavior of liquid helium at very low temperatures.

1.2.4 The "Ergodic Theorem" and "Equally Probable States"

It is a basic assumption in the Boltzmann-Planck equation, Eq. 2, that each permissible "microscopic" state contributing to Ω is to be regarded as equally probable. To the theoretical specialist this sort of assumption has always offered a challenge. Various attempts were made over the years to prove that this assumption of equally probable "microscopic" states could follow from classical mechanics without additional assumptions, and these efforts involve discussions of the so-called "Ergodic Theorem." Planck says straightforwardly: "In dynamics the concept of probability plays no part or, as we may say, '*all microscopic* states are equally probable in dynamics.'" On the other hand, we can perhaps adopt the point of view that the assumption is made *faute de mieux*, and that the fundamental Eq. 2 is justified by the success of the resulting theory. Thus Rushbrooke (1949) starts from the point of view that

> "For the present we must regard the validity of [Eq. 2] as ultimately resting on the agreement of theoretical results deduced from it with experimental data. . . . In the absence of any indication to the contrary, we can only assume that '*all conceivable different micromolecular* states of the assembly (complexions) corresponding to the same values of E, V, and N, are equally probable.*' This hypothesis underlies the whole of statistical mechanics and, like [Eq. 2], must, for the present, be regarded as justified *a posteriori*, by the success of the theory based on it."

So Rushbrooke.

Interpretation of Irreversible Processes. The difficulties that can arise in accepting Eq. 2 appear to lie largely in understanding how to interpret the significance of *irreversible* processes in terms of statistical mechanics. The ergodic theorem implies that "in the course of time a system really passes through *all* the microscopic states corresponding to its macroscopic conditions" (Planck). Planck points out that at first sight this appears unacceptable in relation to what we know of thermodynamics, because it appears to imply that a system will spon-

* "Micromolecular" state is an alternative to "microscopic" state, as used in this book. Correspondingly, "distinguishable complexions" is an alternative to "distinguishable configurations."

taneously assume configurations which we are led to believe from our observations of nature simply do *not* arise spontaneously. Thus, for example, if we place a lump of ice in a beaker of warm water, classical thermodynamics (and experience!) states emphatically that the ice will warm up and that the water will cool down, and never vice versa. On the other hand, since cooling of the ice and warming of the water correspond to conceivable microscopic configurations which are still consistent with a given value of the total energy E, our foundation stone of statistical mechanics suggests that this situation can arise spontaneously.

We can remove these worries summarily by saying simply that the permissible microscopic configurations corresponding to the ice warming up and the water cooling down are so vastly more numerous in number than those corresponding to the reverse situation that our chance of observing the ice cool down spontaneously in nature around us is fantastically remote, but presumably not *entirely* impossible.* The general problem is still quite a challenging one today, however, and involves the difficulty of reconciling somehow or other the very common occurrence in nature of quite *irreversible* processes (that is, happenings which definitely "go one way in time," such as birth and death) with an outlook which says that ultimately we should be able to analyze the whole behavior of the physical world in terms of some form of mechanics which is regarded as fundamentally *reversible* in time.†

* We shall see later (cf., e.g., the examples given in Section 1.4 ahead) that the computed probability for one of these "unexpected" macroscopic states to occur spontaneously is really *extraordinarily* small. Suppose now that some usually reliable witness avers that on one occasion he found the water spontaneously heating up and the ice cooling down. The a priori probability, computed by statistical mechanics, for this to happen is so tremendously small that we would surely have to consider carefully the alternative hypothesis that the event had *not* occurred, but that our witness (perhaps even ourselves!) had experienced a brief hallucination. The probability for this hallucination might indeed be very small but almost certainly much greater than the a priori probability for the actual event to occur spontaneously.

We suggest that this sort of comparison might be made more widely when reports are received from isolated witnesses of very improbable events in the world around us.

† There is presumably universal agreement that classical mechanics as a description of nature is reversible in time in the sense that replacing t by $-t$ in Newton's basic equations of motion does *not* alter their essential form. (This is in contrast, for example, to the differential equation of heat conduction.) Alternatively we say that in a classical mechanical system the reversal of the velocity of each and every particle at any instant will then ideally cause the system to "retrace its steps" precisely.

There is perhaps less universal agreement about quantum mechanics (see, e.g.,

Today there is still considerable divergence of opinion among specialists on how this transition from a theory of reversible mechanics to irreversibility in nature should best be made; later we shall outline briefly possible ways of looking at the problem (see Chapter 4), but let us now return to the basic question of equilibrium statistical mechanics resting on Eq. 2 as our foundation.

1.3 A SIMPLE MODEL OF A SOLID

Let us examine forthwith an elementary problem of some importance. Consider a simple model of a paramagnetic solid. We assume that we have N paramagnetic "elements" (similar molecules) distributed in the body,* each element being essentially fixed in space. We assume that each element can exist in two magnetic states (magnetic moment "up" or "down" in relation to some very weak magnetic field defining a direction in space). We assume moreover that the paramagnetic elements are sufficiently far apart in the body that we can neglect in the first place any interaction between them. Finally we assume, at least for the present, that we can ignore any *other* atomic or molecular features of the solid such as atomic or molecular vibrations or rotations. That is to say, the *only* distinct molecular configurations we recognize at present are two possible orientations of each individual magnetic moment.

Born, 1949a). On the one hand, it can be maintained that Schrödinger's wave equation is essentially reversible in time as far as the observable properties of the wave function ψ are concerned. However, in interpreting the behavior on an atomic model, the wave mechanical restrictions presumably prevent us from "reversing" the velocities of the *particles* precisely, so that the system could never retrace its steps perfectly.

In the same way we would argue that the remarkably accurate interpretation of the quantum mechanics of atomic behavior through the use of *probabilities* (work done primarily by Born) must inevitably involve a degree of irreversibility in terms of *atomic* behavior, since a description of events evolving strictly in terms of probability cannot logically be made reversible in time (cf., e.g., Wu and Rivier, 1961).

Professor Born himself (private communication) says today " . . . My feeling is, that in quantum mechanics reversibility cannot be defined simply. Shall one assume that one can reverse all wave amplitudes or only the momenta of particles or what? . . . "

* We shall use N throughout for the (arbitrary, but large) number of elements, or particles, or molecules in an assembly, and $\mathfrak{N}$ for Avogadro's number when we wish specifically to deal with a mole of such elements in an assembly. We have of course $\mathfrak{N}k = R$, where k is Boltzmann's constant and R is the gas constant.

1.3.1 Paramagnetic Salt Model

This assembly is probably the simplest model involving **independent localized elements** and offers a starting point for considering the behavior of a real paramagnetic salt, such as iron ammonium alum or cerium magnesium nitrate, at very low temperatures (roughly 1° or 2°K and below). At these very low temperatures and in such paramagnetic salts, we can generally ignore, to a very good approximation, any contribution from the vibrations of the atomic or molecular lattice to the energy, or entropy, of the body. Precisely because the entropy of such a salt is indeed dominated at these low temperatures by the magnetic properties, and because the entropy (as we shall see) can then be readily controlled with a strong enough external magnetic field, these paramagnetic salts can be used to provide efficient refrigeration at very low temperatures. In all refrigerators we must have a system with a significant entropy content which we can control easily by some external means; at more normal temperatures a gas is the common medium for refrigeration because we can control the entropy readily by altering the external pressure with a compressor.*

1.3.2 The Entropy

We consider then our solid comprising N molecular locations or "sites" in space, each site being occupied by a molecule or "element" which can be in one of two distinct states (magnetic moment "up," state 1; or "down," state 2). If we assume (for the present) that the energy of an element in either of these two states is identical, we can calculate Ω immediately, and hence the entropy S from Eq. 2. More strictly, our energy assumption here means physically that the magnitude of any energy difference between the two states, $|\epsilon_1 - \epsilon_2|$, is very small in comparison with the ("classical") thermal energy, $\sim kT$, available per degree of freedom.† A single microscopic, or micro-

* The late Sir Francis Simon of the Clarendon Laboratory, Oxford, loved to refer to refrigeration as a process of "sucking out the entropy." In this connection he emphasized clearly two requirements for a useful refrigerator at any temperature: not only must we be able to cool the refrigerator itself by sucking out entropy, but there must be plenty of entropy available to be sucked out if the process is to be of any use for cooling other things! Thus apparently promising low-temperature refrigerators may be rather useless in *practice* because they have so little entropy content that even a small heat influx would ruin their operation.

† Starting from a model of strictly *independent* elements with strictly "private" energy levels (say ϵ_i), it is only a first approximation to say that an interaction *between* the elements will simply alter the "private" energy levels, but it is a very useful first approximation.

molecular, configuration of the assembly is represented by a particular series of N "labels," 2 1 1 1 2 2 1 2 . . . , denoting the molecular state (1 or 2) of each of the N molecules or elements. Since, with our present assumptions, the total energy E of the solid is unaffected by any particular arrangement of molecular states, we have only to ask what is the total number of ways, Ω, of labeling these N sites individually with a 1 or a 2. Since each element can exhibit one of two distinct molecular states, we have immediately

$$\Omega = 2^N, \tag{8}$$

and hence the corresponding entropy for the body,

$$S = k \ln 2^N = Nk \ln 2. \tag{9}$$

Very often it is convenient to assume that we are dealing with a mole of "elements"; thus in the present example, setting $N = \mathfrak{N}$ (Avogadro's or Loschmidt's number; $\mathfrak{N} \approx 6 \times 10^{23}$/mole), we have

$$S = R \ln 2 \tag{10}$$

for the entropy per mole of paramagnetic molecules, where R is the gas constant ($R = \mathfrak{N}k \approx 8.3$ joules/deg mole ≈ 2 cal/deg mole).

Now we shall see later (Chapter 3) that the molar entropy of the familiar "ideal gas" is given by

$$S = R\left[\ln \mathcal{V}\left(\frac{2\pi mkT}{h^2}\right)^{3/2} + \frac{5}{2}\right], \tag{11}$$

where $\mathcal{V}$ is the molar volume of the gas, and m is the mass of a gas molecule. For air at N.T.P., Eq. 11 yields an entropy S of about $18R$. The fact that the entropy given by Eq. 10 is a useful fraction of this gaseous entropy provides our initial warrant for using a paramagnetic salt for refrigeration at very low temperatures, since clearly we have a good quantity of entropy available. Now, in Eqs. 9 and 10, S is apparently independent of the temperature T, and this reflects our assumption that the microscopic complexions, or states, are all identical in energy. If, however, we go to some *sufficiently* low temperature, the small interaction energy between individual magnetic moments in our solid must *ultimately* become comparable with kT. When this happens a progressive trend will set in favoring the occupation of the lower energy states; this in turn means that the number of permissible microscopic configurations, Ω, taking into account the over-all energy restrictions, will diminish as the temperature is lowered and therefore S will also diminish. It is of course the business of statistical mechanics, when we have put forward a more detailed model to allow for these energy differences between the individual microscopic states, to predict precisely how the entropy will decay with temperature.

1.3.3 Alteration of Entropy by Magnetic Fields

In order to use a paramagnetic salt for refrigeration, we must be able to alter its entropy at will by some *external* means, and this we can do by applying a sufficiently strong external magnetic field. If we apply a strong magnetic field in the "up" direction, let us say, so that now $\epsilon_2 - \epsilon_1 \gg kT$, this will mean that, for a given total energy of the solid, the occupation of the lower energy levels (magnetic moment "up," state 1) will be greatly favored in calculating Ω. If the magnetic field is sufficiently strong, we may ultimately reach the condition where *only* state 1 is significantly occupied throughout the paramagnetic salt. That is to say, in this limit there is only *one* distinguishable microscopic configuration for the assembly—that each and every element is in state 1. Hence we would now have $\Omega \approx 1$, in Eq. 2, and thus

$$S_H \approx k \ln 1 \approx 0, \qquad (12)$$

where S_H refers to the molar entropy of the salt with the very strong external magnetic field H applied. If we put together what we have outlined so far, we can sketch in a crude qualitative manner, as in Fig. 1, how the entropy at low temperatures of a simple paramagnetic solid should vary with temperature T and with applied magnetic field H.

1.3.4 Introduction of Degeneracy

Let us note one further feature of this particular problem before going on with the general theoretical development. The possible magnetic states in a real paramagnetic salt are often more complex than we have assumed. If we assume that, instead of simply *two* distinct "atomic" states for the magnetic moment of each element, there are g distinct states, which again as a first approximation we

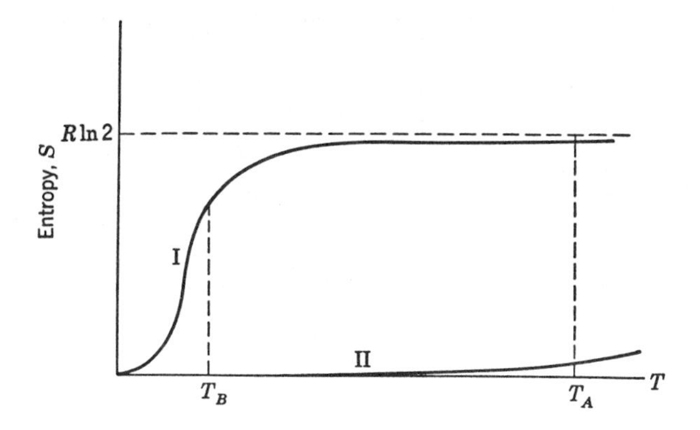

FIG. 1. *Rough sketch* of variation of molar entropy S of idealized paramagnetic salt at low temperatures.

I. Variation of entropy S with temperature T in zero external magnetic field. T_A is a temperature sufficiently high for any interactions involving magnetic energy between elements to be neglected, but also still sufficiently low for lattice vibrational, or rotational, energy to be negligible. T_B indicates a temperature at which the (magnetic) interaction energy between elements becomes significant in comparison with kT.

II. Variation of entropy with temperature in a "very large" external magnetic field H.

assume are all identical in energy (until we go to the very lowest temperatures), it follows immediately that

$$\Omega = g^N, \tag{8a}$$

and consequently the entropy per mole of paramagnetic molecules would then be

$$S = R \ln g. \tag{10a}$$

As long as the g molecular states may be regarded as identical in energy, we may say technically that we are dealing with an atomic or molecular energy level which is "g-fold degenerate."

Appropriate calorimetric measurements of the entropy S of paramagnetic salts at low temperatures may thus enable us, using essentially Eq. 10a, to deduce directly the degeneracy g which can then be compared with theoretical predictions or with other measurements such as spectroscopic data of one kind and another. Figures 2a and 2b show some experimental data on actual paramagnetic salts illustrating this point.

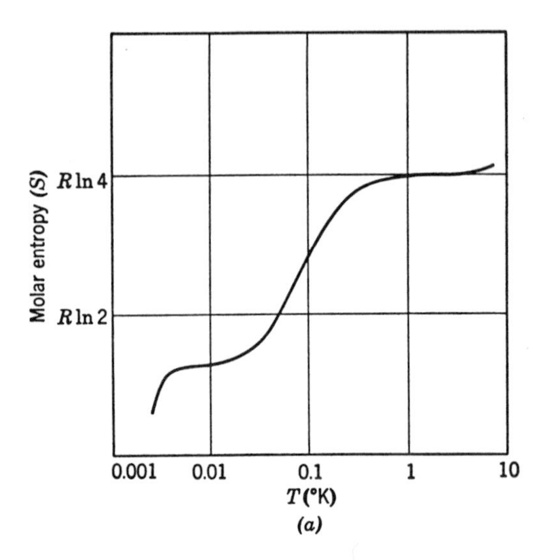

FIG. 2a. Entropy of potassium chromium alum [$KCr(SO_4)_2 \cdot 12H_2O$] (after de Klerk, Steenland, and Gorter, 1949).

Perhaps we should remark that the scale of temperature in this figure is logarithmic.

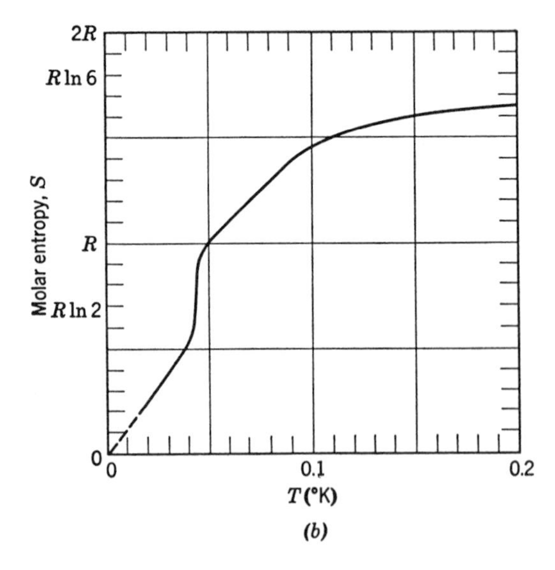

FIG. 2b. Variation of entropy of iron ammonium alum [$FeNH_4(SO_4)_2 \cdot 12H_2O$] at very low temperatures, as determined experimentally by Kürti, Lainé and Simon (1937); (see also Kürti and Simon, 1949).

Note: It appears from subsequent work by A. H. Cooke and his collaborators that in fact the curve requires some modification in detail.

1.4 DISTRIBUTION OF MICROSCOPIC COMPLEXIONS

Let us now look a little more closely at how the total number of complexions, Ω, is actually built up. It may be helpful here to think simply of a collection of N pennies, where now the elementary, or molecular, states 1 and 2 will correspond to "heads" and "tails," the pennies being laid out in a row on a table from left to right. Any one particular arrangement of "heads" or "tails" (such as $H, T, T, H, T, H, H, H, T, H, \ldots$) will thus correspond to one particular "microscopic" configuration of the whole assembly. Let us emphasize now that any question of whether the pennies *themselves* are truly identical or not is actually quite irrelevant to the argument. All that matters is whether a particular place on the table, corresponding to a particular site in the molecular model, is occupied by the "label" H or T.*

Let us now consider imposing some "macroscopic" condition about the over-all ratio of heads to tails in our assembly—e.g., that the *total* number of heads should be equal to the total number of tails. In our paramagnetic solid this would correspond to a macroscopic requirement that the total magnetic moment of the solid be strictly zero. If, for example, we have only two pennies to deal with, then evidently the *total* number of configurations possible for these pennies is four (HH, HT, TH, TT), whereas the number of configurations satisfying our condition of strict equality between "heads" and "tails" is two (HT, TH). More generally, we want to determine how many different microscopic configurations are consistent with some specified *macroscopic* condition or macroscopic state when we are dealing with N "elements" (and N is usually a very large number).

Given then N of these distinct "sites" or "locations" in our molecular model, in how many different ways can they be labeled with n_1 "heads" and n_2 "tails"? (Here of course $n_2 = N - n_1$.) The number of distinguishable ways, ω, of doing this is easily seen to be

$$\omega = \frac{N!}{n_1!n_2!} = \frac{N!}{n_1!(N - n_1)!} \tag{13}$$

(See Appendix I.) Now some specific *number* n_1 of "heads" (and correspondingly n_2 "tails"), irrespective of the particular microscopic *arrangement* of these heads and tails, corresponds in our model of the

* I would take the point of view that atoms, or molecules, of the same type, or electrons for that matter, whether considered classically or quantum mechanically are, of *themselves*, indistinguishable—and always have been! All that is ever distinguishable about them, when we count the number of configurations, is some form of "label" determining what state an atom, molecule, or electron is in.

paramagnetic salt to a particular value of the macroscopic, over-all, magnetic moment $\mathfrak{M}$. More specifically,

$$\mathfrak{M} = (n_1 - n_2)\mathfrak{m} = (2n_1 - N)\mathfrak{m}, \tag{14}$$

where $\mathfrak{m}$ is the magnetic moment of a single element, assumed positive when in the "up" direction (state 1) and negative when "down" (state 2), and ω of Eq. 13 then tells us the number of distinct microscopic configurations of the assembly which correspond to this macroscopic magnetic moment $\mathfrak{M}$. In other words (following Boltzmann and Planck), ω will determine the relative probability that such a particular macroscopic state will occur spontaneously in the equilibrium condition with no externally applied magnetic field. Clearly the maximum possible value of $\mathfrak{M}$ is $N\mathfrak{m}$ (all "heads"!), and for this very particular state we have obviously $\omega = 1$ (Eq. 13 with $n_1 = N$). Therefore the relative probability P for this to occur "spontaneously" in the equilibrium state is $P = \omega/\Omega$, where Ω is the *total* number of possible microscopic configurations, and in our simple model $\Omega = 2^N$. If we now consider again a particle of solid matter of about 10^{-3}mm^3 volume as mentioned earlier, then perhaps $N \sim 10^{16}$, and thus $P = 2^{-10^{16}} \sim 10^{-3\times 10^{15}}$. We can justly say that this is a quite inconceivably small number, and we can therefore dismiss with supreme confidence any possibility that, in macroscopic thermodynamic equilibrium with zero applied magnetic field, the particle of paramagnetic salt would ever exhibit *spontaneously* the saturation magnetic moment, $\mathfrak{M} = N\mathfrak{m}$.

But probably this suggestion of a spontaneous *saturation* magnetic moment seems much too drastic. Let us ask rather what is our chance of observing a spontaneous net magnetic moment only one-millionth part (10^{-6}), or greater, of the saturation magnetic moment under the same conditions. In Appendix I, Section 2, we see that now

$$\omega \approx \frac{2^N}{\sqrt{\pi}}\frac{e^{-10^4}}{2.10^2} \tag{15a}$$

and hence

$$P = \frac{\omega}{\Omega} \approx \frac{e^{-10^4}}{3.10^2} \sim \frac{1}{10^{4\times 10^3}}. \tag{15b}$$

This value for P is still fantastically small; if we assume that each microscopic configuration persists for about 10^{-9} sec,* and that the

* I am told that this is not a grossly unreasonable value to assume for some paramagnetic salts.

age of the earth approaches 10^{10} years, then the total number of complexions that would occur during the whole history of the earth would be less than 10^{27}. This number is still so trivial compared with $10^{4 \times 10^3}$ (cf. Eq. 15*b*) that the chance of a single configuration, which would correspond to a magnetic moment of the required magnitude, occurring spontaneously and at any time during the whole history of the earth remains entirely negligible.

This sort of example serves to illustrate the general rule that the vast majority of microscopic configurations correspond extremely closely to what we normally think of as the macroscopic equilibrium state. Thus in our paramagnetic salt we think of the macroscopic equilibrium state under zero applied magnetic field as implying $\mathfrak{M}$ strictly zero. Our example shows that any marked spontaneous deviation from $\mathfrak{M} = 0$ is enormously improbable even when dealing with a rather small speck of matter. So in statistical mechanics we can generally assume that only complexions in the vicinity of the "most probable" configurations are of any real significance, and indeed this enables us to calculate the entropy S for more complex molecular models from a quite elementary standpoint by calculating only the contribution of the "most probable" configurations to $\ln \Omega$, rather than attempting to compute strictly the *total* number of configurations involved.* The general trend in behavior of the possible molecular

* (i) Actually it is possible to carry through the general calculation of Ω rather more strictly in terms of the *total* number of configurations using the analytical method of "steepest descents," and this foundation for statistical mechanics we owe to Darwin and Fowler (cf. Fowler, 1936). We might note, however, that Born (1949b, p. 162) maintains that "the two methods . . . do not differ as much as it appears. Both use asymptotic approximations . . . either . . . before averaging, or . . . after averaging. The results are completely identical. Yet there are apostles and disciples for each of the two doctrines who regard their creed as the only orthodox one. In my opinion it is just a question of training and practice which formalism is more convenient."

(ii) For many purposes, and in particular for the direct applications of equilibrium statistical mechanics, we can indeed, with confidence, neglect entirely the "less probable" molecular configurations, or in other words ignore any significant departures from the assumed macroscopic equilibrium configuration. But the existence of *observable* spontaneous fluctuations under certain circumstances (Brownian Movement or "noise" more generally) points out that these less probable configurations cannot be *universally* ignored. It is perhaps remarkable that sufficiently delicate, but yet macroscopically observable, physical systems do indeed exist, for which we also have sensitive enough amplifying means (e.g., microscopes or electronic amplifiers), to enable us to observe these spontaneous fluctuations if we set out to do so. I would argue moreover that these very "spontaneous fluctuations" are of great importance in an understanding of irreversible processes (cf. e.g., MacDonald, 1962, and see also Section 4.4).

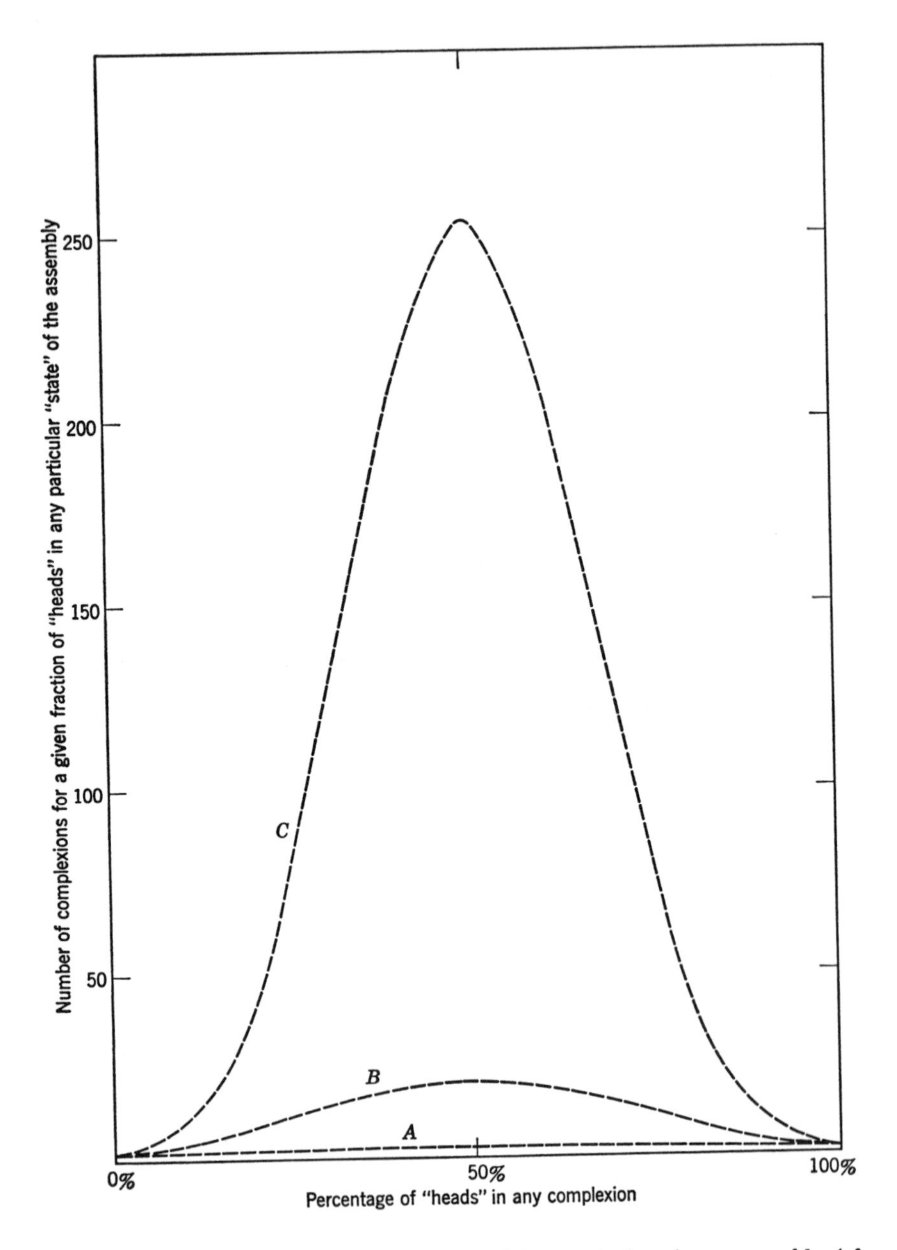

FIG. 3. Sketches to illustrate how the possible complexions in an assembly (of pennies) "pile up" around the "most probable" complexions, as the number of elements (pennies) in the assembly is increased. The "most probable" complexions in each assembly are of course those with 50% "heads," 50% "tails."

The curves are drawn in broken lines as a reminder that, strictly, the ordinate

configurations, together with the general accumulation in the vicinity of the "most probable" state, is illustrated in Fig. 3 (see also Table 1).

TABLE 1

Number of Pennies in Assembly	Ω_{max}, Number of Complexions in *Most Probable* "State" (i.e., exactly equal number of heads and tails, irrespective of order)		Ω, *Total* Number of Possible Complexions	
	Ω_{max}	$\ln \Omega_{max}$	Ω	$\ln \Omega$
2	2	0.693	4	1.386
4	6	1.792	16	2.773
6	20	2.996	64	4.159
8	70	4.250	256	5.545
10	252	5.529	1024	6.93
100	$1.0_1 \times 10^{29}$	66.7_8	$1.2_7 \times 10^{30}$	69.3_1

1.5 BASIC RESULTS

When we consider more complex and general molecular systems, two new features arise which make the analysis more difficult. First, there may be *many* states possible for each individual molecule, rather than just the two ("heads" and "tails") usually considered in our discussion so far. And secondly, these different individual molecular states will generally correspond to significantly different energy levels. We consider a solid more generally as an isolated assembly of "elements" (atoms or molecules), each localized at some particular position or "site" in the solid, each element capable of assuming altogether say l different states, and each state of an element corresponding to some energy, say ϵ_i, together with the requirements that the *total* number of elements in the assembly is N, say, and the *total* energy

only exists at discrete values of the abscissa [e.g., in Curve A only at 0% (both "tails"), 50% (one "head," one "tail"), and 100% (both "heads")].

A. An assembly of two pennies.

B. An assembly of six pennies.

C. An assembly of ten pennies.

(See also Table 1.)

of the isolated assembly is E. Here N and E are to be regarded as constants.

In any particular complexion of the assembly, let us say there are n_1 of the elements each in state 1 with energy ϵ_1, n_2 each in state 2 with energy ϵ_2, etc.; then we may regard our basic problem in statistical mechanics as the evaluation of

$$S = k \ln \Omega, \qquad \text{i.e., Eq. 2} \tag{16}$$

where Ω is the total number of distinct microscopic configurations, or complexions, of the assembly, subject always to

$$\sum_i n_i = N \tag{16a}*$$

$$\sum_i n_i \epsilon_i = E, \tag{16b}*$$

where the summations are taken over all possible energy states of an element. Generally speaking, the individual energy levels ϵ_i may be considered as dependent on some macroscopic parameter such as the volume V of the body, or in a paramagnetic salt would depend more directly on the external magnetic field H. If we assume that the volume V is the dominant external parameter, then our basic problem as outlined means that we are seeking to find the thermodynamic entropy S as a function of the energy E, volume V, and number of elements involved, N.

As we have indicated earlier, it is entirely adequate when we are dealing with a number of elements, N, which is very large (as in any typical solid or gaseous problem) simply to evaluate $\ln \Omega$ in Eq. 16 from the number of configurations, say $\Omega_{\max}$, corresponding to the "most probable" state of the assembly, rather than attempting to evaluate the *total* number of configurations. Table 1 illustrates how $\ln \Omega_{\max}$ becomes a rapidly better approximation to $\ln \Omega$ as the number of elements in the assembly is increased (and remember that in Table 1 the largest value of N is only a mere 10^2). This approxi-

* These apparently rather simple "restrictive conditions" are actually very vital in the physics of our whole problem. Equation 16*a* really expresses what we mean in statistical mechanics by "atoms" or "particles" (i.e., conservation of total number N), whereas Eq. 16*b* expresses the very concept of arriving at a condition of thermal equilibrium in an isolated system (i.e. that particles in different elementary states can exchange energy freely with one another so long as the *total* energy E is unchanged).

The significance of the restrictive conditions is mentioned again specifically when we consider the statistics of photons; see p. 112, second footnote.

mation makes the problem a straightforward matter of seeking for a conditional maximum (of number of configurations) using differential calculus, subject to the restrictive conditions of Eqs. 16*a* and 16*b*. The analysis is outlined in Appendix II, and yields ultimately the result for the entropy S that

$$S = k\left[N \ln \sum_i \exp(-\epsilon_i/kT) + E/kT\right],$$

or, for a mole of the substance,

$$S = R \ln \sum_i \exp(-\epsilon_i/kT) + E/T, \tag{17}$$

where E is of course now the energy per mole.

Now in thermodynamics we define the Helmholtz free energy F by

$$F = E - TS, \tag{18}$$

and consequently from Eq. 17 we have for the Helmholtz free energy per mole

$$F = -RT \ln \sum_i \exp(-\epsilon_i/kT) \tag{19}$$

i.e.,

$$\boxed{F = -RT \ln Z}, \tag{20}$$

where the "partition function" (per element) Z (see also Section 1.5.1) is defined by

$$\boxed{Z = \sum_i \exp(-\epsilon_i/kT)}. \tag{20a}$$

Equation 20 is really a foundation stone for many statistical mechanical calculations and enables us to calculate thermodynamic parameters readily if we can evaluate the "partition function" Z. Thus

$$E = F + TS = -T^2 \frac{\partial}{\partial T}\left(\frac{F}{T}\right)_V \tag{21a}$$

and, using Eq. 20 for F, we have for the internal energy per mole

$$E = \frac{RT^2}{Z}\left(\frac{\partial Z}{\partial T}\right). \tag{21b}$$

In turn, this yields the specific heat at constant volume:

$$C_V = \left(\frac{\partial E}{\partial T}\right)_V. \tag{21c}$$

Moreover, if we accept Eq. 20 for the Helmholtz free energy as our basic starting point, we can then regard the entropy S also as a *derived* quantity, i.e.,

$$S = -\left(\frac{\partial F}{\partial T}\right)_V, \tag{22a}$$

and thus, using Eq. 20, we find for the molar entropy in terms of the partition function Z

$$S = R \ln Z + \frac{RT}{Z}\frac{\partial Z}{\partial T}. \tag{22b}$$

Since we can also write

$$C_V = T\left(\frac{\partial S}{\partial T}\right)_V,$$

we can therefore also, as an alternative to Eq. 21c, derive the specific heat directly from F:

$$C_V = -T\left(\frac{\partial^2 F}{\partial T^2}\right), \tag{22c}$$

or in turn we can write for the molar specific heat directly in terms of Z:

$$C_V = R\left[\frac{2T}{Z}\frac{\partial Z}{\partial T} - \frac{T^2}{Z^2}\left(\frac{\partial Z}{\partial T}\right)^2 + \frac{T^2}{Z}\frac{\partial^2 Z}{\partial T^2}\right]. \tag{22d}$$

Finally, if we know the dependence of Z on V (more specifically the energy levels ϵ_i as a function of V), we can readily derive the other important thermodynamic quantities. Thus for example the bulk modulus* B is given by

$$B = -V\left(\frac{\partial p}{\partial V}\right)_T = V\left(\frac{\partial^2 F}{\partial V^2}\right)_T \tag{23a}$$

and so, using Eq. 20 again, we have

$$B = \frac{RTV}{Z}\left[\frac{1}{Z}\left(\frac{\partial Z}{\partial V}\right)_T^2 - \left(\frac{\partial^2 Z}{\partial V^2}\right)_T\right]. \tag{23b}$$

* We shall follow Zemansky (1943), whose text on thermodynamics it would be difficult to better, in the choice of symbols for bulk modulus (B) and volume coefficient of thermal expansion (β), but we shall use χ for the compressibility.

1.5.1 The "Partition Function," or "Zustandsumme"

In English texts the function Z is known as the "partition function," presumably because the vital factor involved, $\exp(-\epsilon_i/kT)$ (usually called the Boltzmann factor), determines in these problems how the individual elements of an assembly are distributed, or "partitioned," over the individual energy states. In German literature the function Z is known as the "Zustandsumme." The partition function is readily generalized to models assumed to obey classical mechanics (see Chapter 4) and then to situations where the energies of the individual "elements" are not immediately separable from one another as we have assumed here.

1.5.2 The "Internal Distribution" and Degeneracy

For evaluating the over-all macroscopic thermodynamic properties of our solid, we require the partition function Z, which involves the summation over the Boltzmann factor. But en route to the macroscopic result for the entropy, Eq. 17, or for the Helmholtz free energy, Eq. 20, we find that in the "most probable" configurations (i.e., those that occur almost certainly at any time) the individual elements of the assembly are distributed among the possible molecular, or atomic, energy levels ϵ_i according to the law

$$\frac{n_i}{N} = \frac{\exp(-\epsilon_i/kT)}{\sum\limits_i \exp(-\epsilon_i/kT)} \tag{24}$$

(see Appendix II, Eq. 190, with $\beta = -1/kT$). Thus for our solid in thermodynamic equilibrium, the Boltzmann factor appearing in the numerator of Eq. 24 determines what may be called the "internal distribution" of the individual elements over the various energy levels ϵ_i. Now Eq. 24 and Eqs. 17 and 19 are only correct as they stand for systems in which only one distinguishable individual state of a molecule (or atom) corresponds to *each* molecular (or atomic) energy level ϵ_i. More generally, one energy level ϵ_i may correspond to a number (say g_i) of distinguishable molecular states. To take a simple example, an isolated atom vibrating harmonically with a certain amplitude would correspond to a certain energy ϵ, but its axis of vibration might point in a number of different, and distinguishable, directions in space, the energy of vibration, however, being the same. The number g_i is known as the "degeneracy," or "statistical weight," or "quantum weight" to be attached to a particular energy state ϵ_i. We can then again carry through our basic analysis in detail with the explicit inclusion of degeneracy factors g_i, as outlined at the close of Appendix II. Alternatively, it is almost obvious that the modified basic equation for the molar entropy will now read

$$S = R \ln \sum_i g_i \exp(-\epsilon_i/kT) + E/T. \qquad (17a)$$

If we now redefine the partition function per element Z more generally as

$$\boxed{Z = \sum_i g_i \exp(-\epsilon_i/kT)}, \qquad (20b)$$

we may write as before for the molar Helmholtz free energy

$$\boxed{F = -RT \ln Z}. \qquad (20)$$

And indeed all equations involving Z which lead to thermodynamic quantities, such as Eqs. 20, 21, 22, and 23, thus remain formally unchanged, so long as we use Eq. 20*b* for the "partition function" Z.

For the internal distribution we now have in place of Eq. 24

$$\boxed{\frac{n_i}{N} = \frac{g_i \exp(-\epsilon_i/kT)}{\sum_i g_i \exp(-\epsilon_i/kT)}}. \qquad (24a)$$

Moreover, since $E = \sum_i n_i \epsilon_i$, we can write rather directly for the internal energy of the assembly

$$\boxed{E = \frac{N \sum_i \epsilon_i g_i \exp(-\epsilon_i/kT)}{\sum_i g_i \exp(-\epsilon_i/kT)}}, \qquad (25)$$

alternatively to Eq. 21*b* for E.

It is the job of *mechanics* itself to tell us, for any given model that we propose for a molecular system, what the appropriate values are for the factors g_i, and it is also of course the job of mechanics to tell us for that model the permissible energy levels ϵ_i which are compatible with any boundary conditions we impose.

1.6 "INTERNAL EXCITATION" OF SOLIDS—SCHOTTKY ANOMALY

Let us now apply some of our results. Consider first a solid composed of N similar atoms or molecules, supposedly at sufficiently low temperatures that we may once again neglect any vibrational contribution to the energy. Let us assume that each element (atom or molecule) can exist, independent of any others, in a few distinct localized states of energy ϵ_i. In the simplest case let us assume only two energy levels for each element, ϵ_1 and ϵ_2, both nondegenerate ($g_1 = g_2 = 1$). If we care to assume that these two states correspond to magnetic orientations of an atom or molecule, this could offer a second approximation to the model of a paramagnetic salt at low temperatures, but in principle the energy levels might correspond to any other type of localized atomic states with a limited number of possible "excited" energy levels. Then we have for the partition function per element

$$Z = e^{-\epsilon_1/kT} + e^{-\epsilon_2/kT}, \tag{26}$$

and thus for the Helmholtz free energy per mole

$$F = -RT \ln (e^{-\epsilon_1/kT} + e^{-\epsilon_2/kT}), \tag{27}$$

and also for the internal energy per mole

$$E = N \frac{\epsilon_1 e^{-\epsilon_1/kT} + \epsilon_2 e^{-\epsilon_2/kT}}{e^{-\epsilon_1/kT} + e^{-\epsilon_2/kT}}, \tag{28a}$$

either using Eq. 21*b* or directly from Eq. 25. Thus

$$E = N \frac{\epsilon_1 + \epsilon_2 e^{-\epsilon/kT}}{1 + e^{-\epsilon/kT}}, \tag{28b}$$

or

$$E - N\epsilon_1 = N \frac{\epsilon e^{-\epsilon/kT}}{1 + e^{-\epsilon/kT}},$$

where $\epsilon = \epsilon_2 - \epsilon_1$.

1.6.1 Dependence on Temperature and Volume

The temperature-dependence of E involves only the ratio ϵ/kT, and this factor can be conveniently rewritten as θ_S/T where θ_S is a "characteristic temperature"* defined by $\theta_S = \epsilon/k$. In general, when we can make this kind of identification in a problem, leading to a

* The subscript S on θ refers to Walther Schottky (Schottky, 1921, 1922).

single "characteristic temperature" describing its behavior, we can then immediately recognize two important limiting regions.

(1) "Low temperatures," i.e., such that $T \ll \theta_S$, for which in our present problem we have from Eq. 28*b*

$$E \approx N(\epsilon_1 + \epsilon e^{-\theta_s/T}), \quad \text{i.e., } E \to N\epsilon_1, \text{ as } T \to 0. \tag{28c}$$

(2) "High temperatures,"* where $T \gg \theta_S$, and we have here

$$E \approx \frac{N}{2}(\epsilon_1 + \epsilon_2). \tag{28d}$$

Equations 28*c* and 28*d* express physically the two limiting situations that, on the one hand, at sufficiently low temperatures we expect that every element of the assembly will ultimately sink into its lowest energy state (ϵ_1), whereas, at sufficiently high temperatures (i.e., where the thermal energy becomes large compared with the energy difference ϵ) we expect the elements will be equally distributed† between the two levels. It is in this limit that the energy spacing between the levels ultimately becomes unimportant ($\epsilon \ll kT$), and we should then expect that our earlier prediction for the molar entropy, i.e., $S = R \ln 2$ (cf. Eq. 10), will be approached. We can readily derive S for our model from Eq. 27 using $S = -\partial F/\partial T$, and in the two limiting regions of temperature we find

(1) "Low temperatures" ($T \ll \theta_S$):

$$S \approx R(\theta_S/T)e^{-\theta_s/T}; \tag{29a}$$

(2) "High temperatures" ($T \gg \theta_S$):

$$S \approx R \ln(1 + e^{-\theta_s/T}) \approx R \ln 2, \tag{29b}$$

and we see from the latter equation that S does indeed approach the limit $R \ln 2$ for this model at high temperatures. On the other hand, Eq. 29*a* indicates that $S \to 0$ as $T \to 0$ (more specifically for $T/\theta_S \ll 1$).

* Although we must write $T \gg \theta$ for the strict mathematical limit of "high temperatures," in models involving a characteristic temperature it is usually sufficient in practice to satisfy the condition $T \gtrsim \theta$. On the other hand, it is very necessary to satisfy adequately the condition $T \ll \theta$ to reach the true "low temperature" region.

† More properly, we should say that the elements are entirely *randomly* distributed between the two states 1 and 2 when the energy difference becomes negligible (in comparison with the available thermal energy per elment). However, as pointed out earlier, when we are dealing with very large numbers of elements, the "most probable" configurations (i.e., here involving essentially an *equal* distribution between the two states) will be entirely dominant.

1.6.2 Agreement with the Third Law

This decay of S toward zero at sufficiently low temperatures is in agreement with the general predictions of the Third Law of Thermodynamics, which originally stems from Nernst's so-called "Heat Theorem." Alternatively, since $F = E - TS$, we may say that at sufficiently low temperatures F and E approach the same common limit, and $\partial F/\partial T$ approaches zero. It is satisfying that the detailed theory of statistical mechanics is found to be in full agreement with the general demands of the Third Law of Thermodynamics when we are dealing with systems in thermal equilibrium. Moreover, statistical mechanics when applied to any particular model makes clear quantitatively what is meant by the general limit "$T \to 0$" as specified by the Third Law of Thermodynamics.

1.6.3 Energy and Specific Heat (the "Schottky Anomaly")

From Eq. 28*b* we can readily plot how the energy E varies in detail with temperature, and by differentiating we can also derive the behavior of the specific heat (see Figs. 4*b* and 4*c*; Fig. 4*a* shows the entropy). The specific heat is seen to rise and fall, passing through a maximum which corresponds, broadly speaking, to the temperature region where the elements are being strongly excited to the higher energy level ϵ_2. This behavior is often known as a "Schottky anomaly" (Schottky, 1921, 1922). More complex specific heat anomalies of this general character will occur if we have to deal with a more complicated energy spectrum of excited molecular or atomic energy levels. Thus, for example, if we assume the existence of three energy levels ϵ_1, ϵ_2, and ϵ_3, where say $\epsilon_3 - \epsilon_1 = 10(\epsilon_2 - \epsilon_1)$, and we assume degeneracies $g_3 = 2$, $g_2 = g_1 = 1$, then an entropy, internal energy, and specific heat will result as shown in Figs. 5*a*, 5*b*, and 5*c*. In Figs. 6*a* and 6*b* we have reproduced the *measured* specific heat of two paramagnetic salts at very low temperatures, and the broad resemblance to these "Schottky anomalies" is evident. Before leaving the "Schottky anomaly," we should point out that in an assembly of localized elements, each with a limited number of permissible energy levels of this type, the specific heat at sufficiently high temperatures should always decay as T^{-2}; thus specifically in the simple case of elements with two nondegenerate energy levels, we have for the molar specific heat when $T \gg \theta_S$

$$C \approx \tfrac{1}{4}R\left(\frac{\theta_S}{T}\right)^2. \tag{30}$$

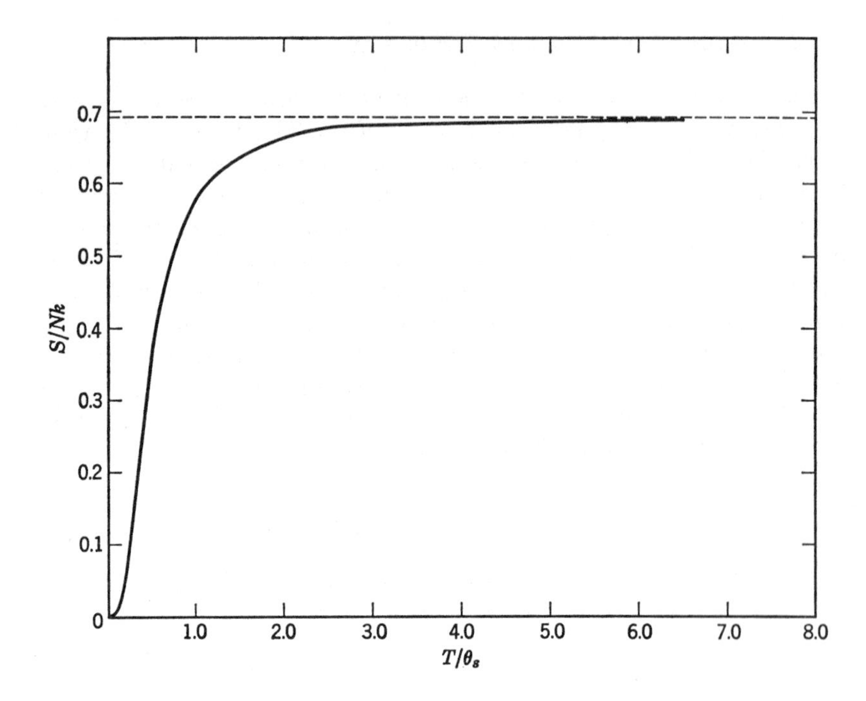

FIG. 4*a*. Variation of entropy S with temperature T arising from a simple Schottky anomaly in an assembly of N elements. If $N = \mathfrak{N}$, we have the entropy per mole of elements, and the ordinate is then simply S/R. At sufficiently high temperatures, $(T/\theta_s \gg 1)$ the limiting value of the ordinate is $\ln 2 = 0.693_1$ (cf. Eq. 29*b*).

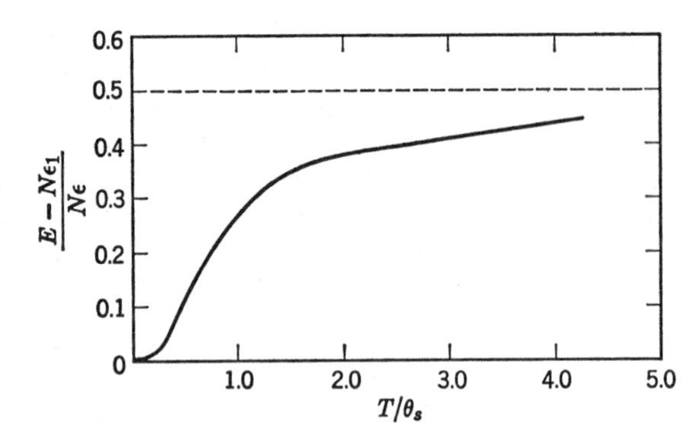

FIG. 4*b*. Variation of internal energy E with temperature T arising from a simple Schottky anomaly in an assembly of N elements. The ordinate as actually plotted is $(E - N\epsilon_1)/N\epsilon$, where $\epsilon = \epsilon_2 - \epsilon_1$. At sufficiently high temperatures, $(T/\theta_s \gg 1)$ the limiting value of the ordinate is 0.5, i.e., $E \rightarrow (N/2)(\epsilon_1 + \epsilon_2)$.

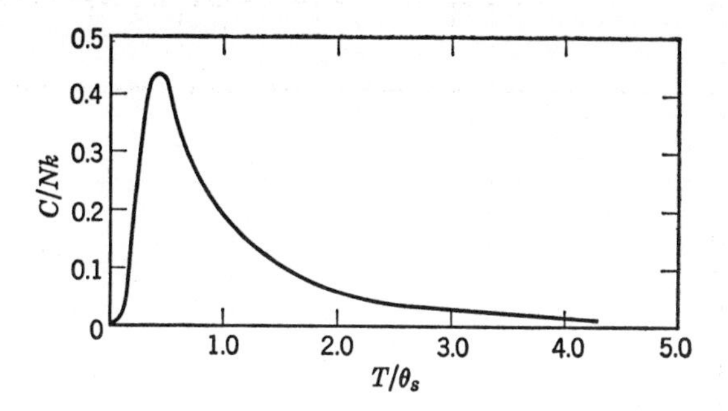

FIG. 4c. Specific heat C arising from a simple Schottky anomaly in an assembly of N elements. If $N = \mathfrak{N}$, we have the specific heat per mole of elements, and the ordinate is then simply C/R.

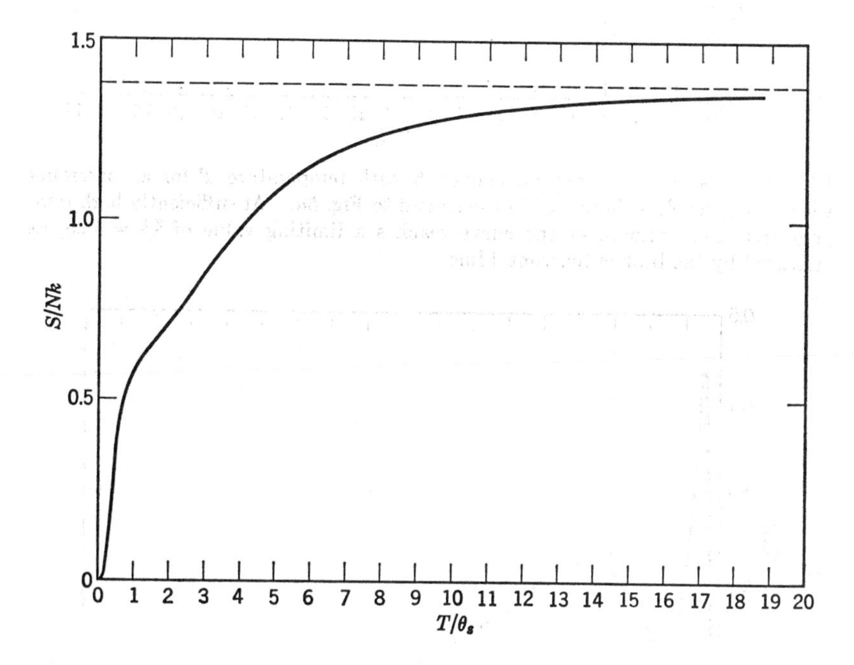

FIG. 5a. Variation of entropy S with temperature T for a more complex type of Schottky anomaly (see Section 1.6.3), where we have *three* energy levels such that $\epsilon_3 - \epsilon_1 = 10\ (\epsilon_2 - \epsilon_1)$; $g_3 = 2$, $g_2 = g_1 = 1$; and we define $k\theta_s = \epsilon_2 - \epsilon_1$. As usual, if we write $N = \mathfrak{N}$, we have the entropy per mole of elements, and the ordinate is then S/R. At sufficiently high temperatures, $(T/10\theta_s \gg 1)$ the ordinate of the curve approaches a limiting value of $\ln 4 = 1.386$, as indicated by the broken horizontal line.

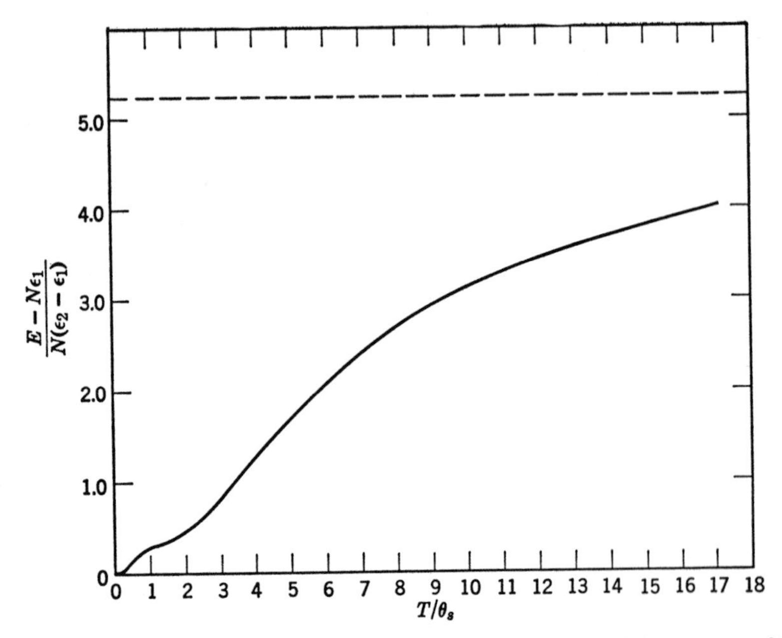

FIG. 5*b*. Variation of internal energy E with temperature T for an assembly with energy levels as indicated in the legend to Fig. 5*a*. At sufficiently high temperatures, the ordinate of the curve reaches a limiting value of $\frac{21}{4} = 5.25$, as indicated by the broken horizontal line.

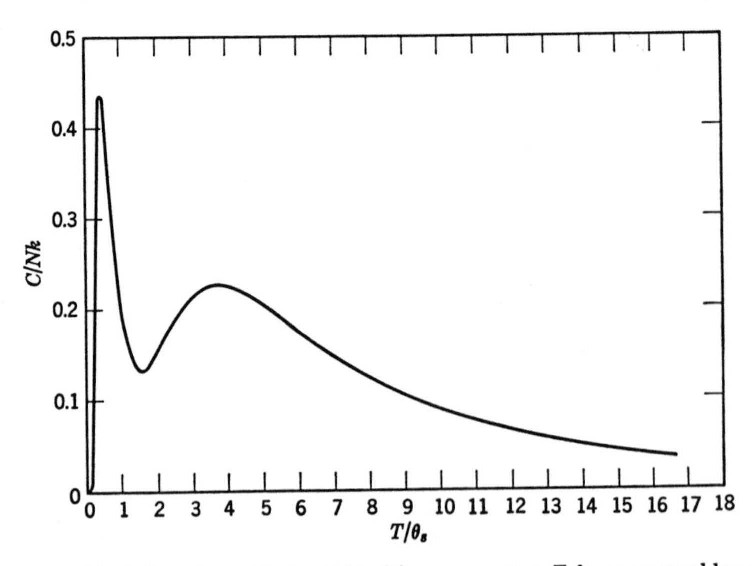

FIG. 5*c*. Variation of specific heat C with temperature T for an assembly with energy levels as indicated in the legend to Fig. 5*a*. As usual, if we write $N = \mathfrak{N}$, the ordinate becomes the specific heat per mole of elements, i.e., C/R.

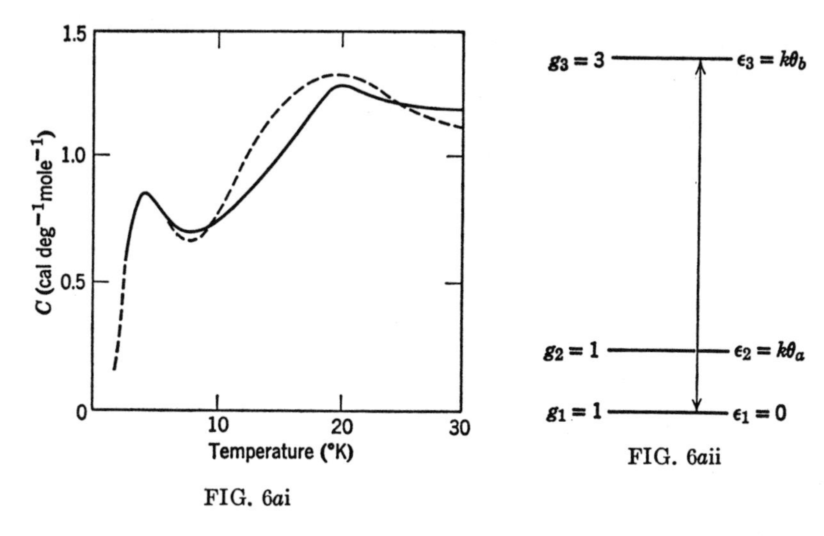

FIG. 6*a*-i and 6*a*-ii. Comparison of experimental and theoretical specific heat of the paramagnetic salt, ferrous ammonium sulfate (after Hill and Smith, 1953).

FIG. 6*a*-i. Component of specific heat arising from magnetic properties of the ferrous ion.

Full curve. Specific heat as deduced from experimental data.

Broken curve. As predicted by Hill and Smith from proposed energy levels of Fe^{2+} ion in ferrous ammonium sulfate (see Fig. 6*a*-ii).

FIG. 6*a*-ii. Energy levels and degeneracies proposed by Hill and Smith for Fe^{2+} ion in ferrous ammonium sulfate; we set the lowest energy level as zero ($\epsilon_1 = 0$) for convenience. $\theta_a = 9.4^0$K and $\theta_b = 56^0$K (or, in a spectroscopist's language, the energy spacing between first and second levels is 6.5 cm^{-1} and between first and third 38 cm^{-1}). Thus the theoretical partition function per element is $Z = 1 + e^{-\theta_a/T} + 3e^{-\theta_b/T}$.

This decay of the specific heat with T^{-2} at temperatures well *above* the maximum region of the anomaly is often very valuable for indicating whether experimental measurements should be extended to lower temperatures in order to seek for such anomalies that would point out internal excitations of this type.

Moreover let us note that Eq. 29*b* (applicable to the simplest model) will more generally be replaced at sufficiently high temperatures by

$$S \approx R \ln \sum_i g_i \tag{29c}$$

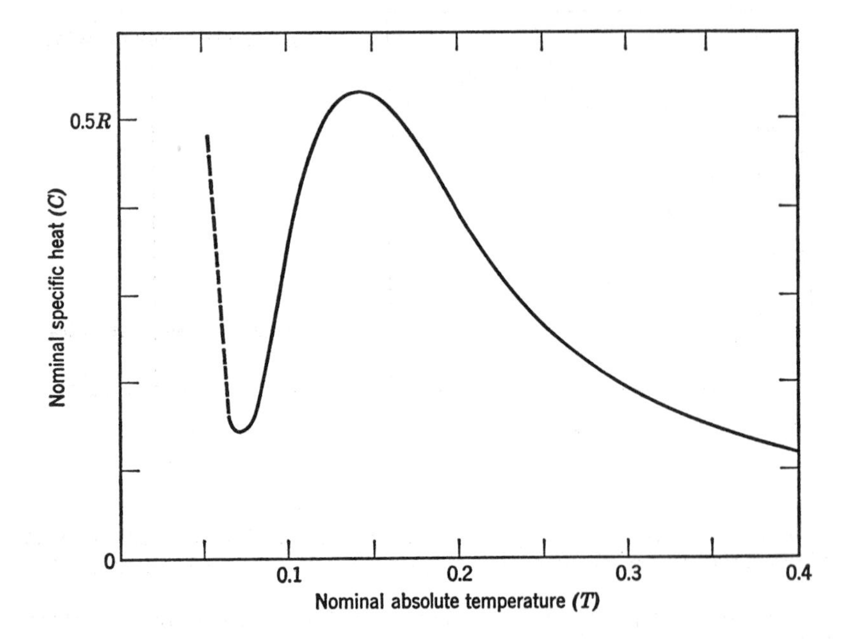

FIG. 6*b*. Specific heat at very low temperature of chromium methylamine alum (after Gardner and Kürti, 1954).

Note: The specific heat and absolute temperature are referred to here as "nominal," because the experimental temperatures are so-called "magnetic temperatures," and some correction would be necessary to yield true absolute temperatures.

1.7 MAGNETIC SUSCEPTIBILITY

Let us consider once more our simplest paramagnetic salt model with only two permissible orientations ("up," state 1, and "down," state 2) of the magnetic moment $\mathfrak{m}$ of an "element" (paramagnetic molecule); both molecular states are assumed to be nondegenerate ($g_1 = g_2 = 1$). We apply an external magnetic field H in the "up" direction, so that a molecule in state (1) will have magnetic energy $-\mathfrak{m}H$ and one in state (2) will have magnetic energy $+\mathfrak{m}H$. Let us further assume that any *other* energy difference between states (1) and (2) is negligible in comparison with the energy difference $2\mathfrak{m}H$. Thus from Eq. 24 the probable number of elements in the two states will be

$$n_1 = N \frac{e^{\mathfrak{m}H/kT}}{e^{\mathfrak{m}H/kT} + e^{-\mathfrak{m}H/kT}}, \tag{31a}$$

$$n_2 = N \frac{e^{-\mathfrak{m}H/kT}}{e^{\mathfrak{m}H/kT} + e^{-\mathfrak{m}H/kT}}. \tag{31b}$$

With each of the n_1 elements in state (1) there is of course associated a magnetic moment $+\mathfrak{m}$, and with each of those in state (2) a magnetic moment of $-\mathfrak{m}$. Consequently the total macroscopic magnetic moment of the solid will be

$$\mathfrak{M} = n_1\mathfrak{m} - n_2\mathfrak{m} = N \frac{\mathfrak{m}e^{\mathfrak{m}H/kT} - \mathfrak{m}e^{-\mathfrak{m}H/kT}}{e^{\mathfrak{m}H/kT} + e^{-\mathfrak{m}H/kT}} \tag{32}$$

We consider now two limits of Eq. 32.

(1) For "low magnetic fields," i.e., $\mathfrak{m}H \ll kT$, we have

$$\mathfrak{M} \approx \frac{N\mathfrak{m}^2 H}{kT}, \tag{33a}$$

or if we define the magnetic susceptibility χ_H as the magnetic moment per unit volume, per unit magnetic field, then

$$\chi_H = \frac{N_1\mathfrak{m}^2}{kT}, \tag{33b}$$

where N_1 is the number of elements per unit volume. Under these circumstances the assembly then obeys Curie's law ($\chi_H \propto T^{-1}$) so long as the temperature is not too low.

(2) On the other hand, for "sufficiently high" magnetic fields (or "sufficiently low" temperatures), i.e., $\mathfrak{m}H \gg kT$, the second term in the numerator and denominator of Eq. 32 becomes negligible, and we have simply

$$\mathfrak{M} \rightarrow N\mathfrak{m}, \tag{34}$$

that is, saturation of the magnetic moment.

For this very simple problem the partition function per element Z is given by

$$Z = e^{\mathfrak{m}H/kT} + e^{-\mathfrak{m}H/kT},$$

and consequently we may write (cf. Eq. 32)

$$\boxed{\mathfrak{M} = N \frac{kT}{Z} \frac{\partial Z}{\partial H} = NkT \frac{\partial \ln Z}{\partial H}}. \tag{35}$$

This expression remains true more generally if we assume that we may write the energy ϵ_i for any molecular energy level as

$$\epsilon_i = \epsilon_i' - \mathfrak{m}_i H, \tag{36}^*$$

where ϵ_i' does *not* involve the magnetic moment of an element, and $\mathfrak{m}_i$ is the component of magnetic moment parallel to the external field H associated with the energy level ϵ_i. In the simple example just given we have written in fact

$$\epsilon_1' = 0, \quad \mathfrak{m}_1 = \mathfrak{m}; \qquad \epsilon_2' = 0, \quad \mathfrak{m}_2 = -\mathfrak{m}.$$

Finally, since we have shown previously that the Helmholtz free energy F for a solid of localized elements can be written

$$F = -NkT \ln Z, \qquad \text{cf. Eq. 20,} \tag{40}$$

it follows that Eq. 35 may also be written, if we wish,† as

$$\boxed{\mathfrak{M} = -\frac{\partial F}{\partial H}}. \tag{41}$$

In the next chapter we consider one of the most important problems in solid-state physics, the vibrations of crystalline solids.

* Although this definition of energy may seem trivially obvious, we should note that it leads to an over-all internal energy E of

$$E = \sum_i n_i \epsilon_i = E' - \mathfrak{M}H, \tag{37}$$

where E' is the total internal energy ignoring magnetic effects. To ensure agreement with this expression, it appears that we must write in formal thermodynamics for the Second Law

$$dE = T\,dS - \mathfrak{M}\,dH, \tag{38}$$

ignoring volume effects. If then as usual we write for the Helmholtz free energy in thermodynamics

$$F = E - TS,$$

then using Eq. 38, we have

$$dF = -S\,dT - \mathfrak{M}\,dH, \tag{39}$$

so that indeed $\mathfrak{M} = -\partial F/\partial H$, in agreement with Eq. 41 in the text.

The important thing to realize is that there is no universal agreement in formal thermodynamics on how the "work" term in the energy equation should be written when external magnetic (or electric) fields are present. What really matters of course is that our "macroscopic" definitions (here Eq. 38) should be consistent with our "microscopic" definitions (here Eq. 36, leading to Eq. 37).

† But see again the preceding footnote.

2

THE VIBRATIONS OF SOLIDS

2.1 NORMAL COORDINATES AND MODES OF VIBRATION

Consider an assembly of N "atoms" or "molecules" which we assume can be regarded as point masses* interacting with one another by some sort of forces. We assume that the whole assembly can take up some position of stable static equilibrium, so that the potential energy V of the whole assembly is then an absolute minimum. We now consider some set of *small* arbitrary displacements of the elements of the assembly from this equilibrium situation. These displacements might be described by the $3N$ Cartesian coordinates† of the elements $(x_1, y_1, z_1, \ldots, x_N, y_N, z_N)$. Then we can always choose a new set of $3N$ coordinates‡ (linear functions of the originals coordinates), say $\xi_1 \cdots \xi_{3N}$, such that the potential energy corresponding to the small arbitrary displacements of the assembly from static equilibrium can be written

$$V(\xi_i) - V_0 = a_1\xi_1^2 + \cdots + a_{3N}\xi_{3N}^2, \tag{42}$$

* This assumption means in effect that we are now concerned only with spatial displacements of the atoms or molecules in contributing to the energy of the solid. In other words, we are now concerned only with vibrational energy, and we are excluding possible rotational motions, or possible "internal excitations" such as we discussed in Section 1.6.

† More strictly, there will really be only $3N - 6$ independent coordinates available to describe an arbitrary displacement from static equilibrium, because 6 coordinates in all are needed to fix the position of the center of gravity of the whole assembly and to fix its orientation in space. However, since N is generally such a very large number, we may safely ignore the 6 in any further discussions.

‡ More strictly, $3N - 6$ coordinates.

where the left-hand side is the net potential energy measured from the minimum V_0 at equilibrium, and the constants a_i are *all positive*. At the same time we can also ensure that the *kinetic* energy of the whole assembly is expressible as a sum of squares of corresponding momentum coordinates, each term again having a positive coefficient.

The fact that we can choose coordinates ξ_i that yield a potential energy which is (for small displacements) simply a sum of independent (positive) terms $a_i\xi_i^2$ (Eq. 42), together with a corresponding quadratic expression for kinetic energy, has a most important consequence. It tells us that, for any given assembly of atoms, a set of $3N$ coordinates (the so-called normal coordinates) always exists in terms of which any arbitrary free motion of the assembly (small displacements!) can be described as that of $3N$ superimposed, *independent*, simple harmonic oscillators—one to each coordinate ξ_i. The reason is of course that the energy of a simple harmonic oscillator is quadratic in its displacement coordinate (potential energy), and naturally also quadratic in the corresponding momentum coordinate (kinetic energy).

Broadly speaking, we may then say that the job of dealing with the vibrations of a solid depends first and foremost on determining these "normal coordinates" for the particular solid concerned (or more specifically in statistical mechanics on determining the frequencies of the corresponding oscillators). In ideal *crystalline* solids the $3N$ simple harmonic oscillators—or "normal modes of vibration" as they are sometimes called—have the form of waves, each with a characteristic wavelength, direction of propagation, and polarization. Let us emphasize three vital features.

(1) The existence of a set of normal coordinates which allows us to describe any arbitrary free (and small!) motion of the solid as arising from the vibrations of a set of $3N$ *independent*, simple harmonic oscillators is a general result of dynamics to which we can appeal without knowing anything about the particular arrangements of the atoms, or the specific crystal structure if we are dealing with a crystalline solid.

(2) The existence of normal coordinates is only strictly valid as long as we are dealing with *small enough* vibrations, in other words under the so-called "harmonic approximation." The next approximation, when the vibrations become larger in amplitude leading to so-called "anharmonic" effects, involves analytically a perturbation of one oscillator by others. The harmonic oscillators are then no longer independent of one another in energy; and the coupling of the oscillators to one another will lead to a variation of their amplitudes of vibration

with time. The "harmonic approximation" is extremely powerful in the physics of solids and can account for many important features, but anharmonic effects must be considered if we are to deal, for example, with thermal expansion (see Sections 2.5 and 2.6 and Section 4.4).

(3) To prove the *existence* of normal coordinates is very different from actually *determining* them specifically for any particular solid. This remains a complicated task today, and consequently models based on rather bold, but convenient, assumptions remain of great value. The two classic models of this type are the Einstein and Debye models for the vibrations of a solid.

2.2 THE EINSTEIN MODEL FOR A CRYSTALLINE SOLID

We have seen that dynamics itself presents us with the *general* result that a stable collection of N "atoms" capable of making *small* vibrations may be represented by a suitable assembly of $3N$ simple harmonic, *independent* oscillators. Einstein (1907) made the simplest assumption that all $3N$ oscillators had the same frequency, say ν_E, and this provides us with the "Einstein model" for the statistical mechanics of the vibrations of a crystalline solid. At first sight it may seem quite natural to identify these oscillators physically with the atoms themselves, each atom being represented by three oscillators, corresponding to the three space coordinates. Essentially this would mean that each atom is supposed to vibrate freely in an individual "cell" of its own without any significant interaction with the vibrations of its neighbors. But the very fact that crystalline solids exist at all implies a strong coupling between an atom and its surrounding neighbors, and Einstein himself (Einstein, 1911) was well aware that the model could only be a first approximation, and that it would be necessary to take into account the coupling of the motion of one atom with those of others. Thus it is on the whole probably safer to regard the Einstein model from the start as being simply the *first approximation* to satisfy *formally* the necessary dynamical requirement of $3N$ harmonic oscillators (so long as we adhere to the restriction of small displacements) without trying to identify more closely the Einstein oscillators with individual atoms.

Wave mechanics then tells us that a harmonic oscillator can only exist in certain stationary states, equally spaced in energy, given by

$$\epsilon_i = (i + \tfrac{1}{2})h\nu_E, \tag{43}$$

where $i = 0, 1, 2, 3, \ldots$, and each level is nondegenerate ($g_i = 1$),* thus:

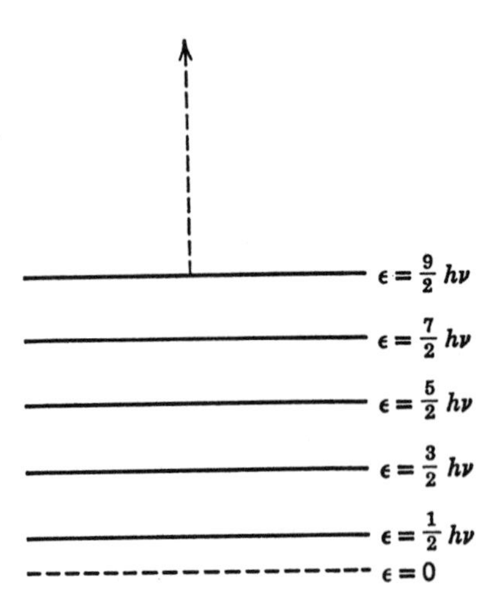

The permitted energy levels (full lines) of a one-dimensional simple harmonic oscillator, as given by quantum mechanics. The energy levels extend upwards at intervals of $h\nu$ without limit. In *classical mechanics* the broken line marked $\epsilon = 0$ would be the minimum energy (no kinetic energy or elastic energy due to displacement) of such an oscillator. The "ground state" of the simple harmonic oscillator lies $h\nu/2$ in energy above this classical minimum energy ($\epsilon = 0$), and this energy difference is the so-called "zero-point energy" of an oscillator.

We can now write down immediately the partition function Z **per oscillator** from Eq. 20a; thus we have

$$Z = \sum_{i=0}^{\infty} e^{-(i+\frac{1}{2})h\nu_E/kT}$$

$$= \frac{e^{-\frac{1}{2}h\nu_E/kT}}{1 - e^{-h\nu_E/kT}}, \tag{44}$$

* Perhaps we should emphasize that we deal throughout, in both the Einstein and Debye models (*vide infra*), with simple harmonic oscillators, each characterized by a *single* displacement variable (together with its associated momentum variable). Thus each of the assembly of $3N$ harmonic oscillators is always, in effect, a "one-dimensional" oscillator. One might also (cf. Rushbrooke, 1949) treat the Einstein model as an assembly of N "three-dimensional" harmonic oscillators, and in that case the degeneracies g_i are not unity but functions of the particular level i. We prefer *not* to do this, since the requirement of $3N$ independent oscillators is a very general one, as we have already pointed out.

noting that Z is just the sum to infinity of a convergent geometrical progression. We see that the simple ratio $h\nu_E/kT$ determines the entire behavior of Z, and hence in turn the behavior of the thermodynamic properties of the Einstein model. This ratio may be conveniently replaced by the ratio θ_E/T, if we define the "(Einstein) characteristic temperature" θ_E by writing $k\theta_E = h\nu_E$. That is,

$$Z = \frac{e^{-\theta_E/2T}}{1 - e^{-\theta_E/T}}. \tag{44a}$$

Thus the Helmholtz free energy per mole of a monatomic solid on the Einstein model is given by

$$F = -3RT \ln Z = \frac{3R\theta_E}{2} + 3RT \ln (1 - e^{-\theta_E/T}), \tag{45}$$

bearing in mind that $3\mathfrak{N}$ oscillators correspond to an assembly of $\mathfrak{N}$ atoms making up a mole of the solid. Hence we have also for the entropy S per mole

$$S = \frac{3R(\theta_E/T)}{e^{\theta_E/T} - 1} + 3R \ln \left(\frac{1}{1 - e^{-\theta_E/T}}\right). \tag{46}$$

At sufficiently low temperatures ($T \ll \theta_E$), we see from Eq. 46 that

$$S \to 0 \quad \left(\text{and } \frac{dS}{dT} \to 0\right); \tag{46a}$$

the vanishing of S as $T \to 0$ is again in agreement with the general predictions of the Third Law of Thermodynamics. At high temperatures ($T \gg \theta_E$) we have

$$S \approx 3R \left[\ln \frac{T}{\theta_E} + 1 \cdot \cdot \cdot\right] \tag{46b}$$

From Eqs. 46*a* and 46*b*, we can immediately derive the limiting behavior of the specific heat per mole at very low, and at high, temperatures; namely, for $T \ll \theta_E$

$$C_V = T \left(\frac{\partial S}{\partial T}\right)_V \to 0, \tag{46c}$$

whereas for $T \gg \theta_E$

$$C_V \approx 3R. \tag{46d}$$

On the one hand, the vanishing of the specific heat at sufficiently low temperatures, which is quite general for any model of the vibrating crystalline solid, is virtually a requirement of the Third Law of

Thermodynamics, and on the molecular scale arises from the ultimate sinking of each of the oscillators into its quantum ground state as we approach absolute zero. On the other hand, Eq. 46*d* is essentially "classical" in form and must also be true for *any* model of a crystalline solid which satisfies the minimum dynamical requirement, for small vibrations, that the stable assembly of N atoms requires $3N$ independent (linear) harmonic oscillators to represent its behavior.

We can also derive the internal energy per mole E (either from Eq. 21*b* or from Eq. 25), and we have

$$E = \frac{3R\theta_E}{2} + \frac{3R\theta_E}{e^{\theta_E/T} - 1}. \tag{47}$$

At very low temperatures we have

$$E = \frac{3R\theta_E}{2}, \tag{47a}$$

independent of temperature; and at sufficiently high temperatures we have

$$E \approx 3RT. \tag{47b}$$

Equation 47*b* is again a "classical" result, in line with the "classical" result (Eq. 46*d*) for the specific heat. Equation 47*a* is an expression for the total (vibrational) "zero-point energy" of the solid, and is a direct consequence of the fact that the ground state for a harmonic oscillator of frequency ν in quantum mechanics is $h\nu/2$ in energy above the classical zero of potential energy* (cf. Eq. 43 with $i = 0$). Let us

* The situation may be viewed in two ways. If we wish *always* to regard a substance as an assembly of particles or *atoms*, defined by appropriate displacement (and momentum) coordinates, it is necessary to recognize that even at absolute zero this assembly has a certain (and very considerable!) amount of energy in *excess* of what a classical (Newtonian) assembly of such atoms would have in the state of minimum potential energy. (This in turn is one way of interpreting physically Heisenberg's Uncertainty Principle:

$$\Delta x\, \Delta p_x \sim h; \tag{48}$$

the minimum *classical* potential energy would require in effect $\Delta x \rightarrow 0$ for each classical "atom," but Eq. 48 would then demand in effect a very large momentum for each "atom.") Thus so long as we wish to use the concept of an assembly of individual atoms, we must also include this zero-point energy, and the zero-point energy is just as "real" as the atoms are in this context.

On the other hand, if we choose to regard properties derived from the over-all *wave function* of an assembly of "atoms" as a more *general* expression of physical "reality," then as we approach absolute zero we shall expect to find the ground state dominantly occupied, and we must then bear in mind that the ground state wave function of an oscillator is not as "featureless" as perhaps we might think from classical mechanics.

also note that Eq. 47 implies that the average energy (say $<\epsilon>$) of a single harmonic oscillator of frequency ν in thermal equilibrium at temperature T is given by

$$<\epsilon> = \frac{h\nu}{2} + \frac{h\nu}{e^{h\nu/kT} - 1}, \qquad (47c)$$

a very frequently used result. We might also say rather colloquially, from Eq. 45, that the average Helmholtz free energy per oscillator (or better the *contribution* per oscillator), say $<f>$, is then

$$<f> = \frac{h\nu}{2} + kT \ln (1 - e^{-h\nu/kT}). \qquad (45a)$$

Using Eq. 21*c*, or alternatively Eqs. 22*c* or 22*d*, we derive immediately for the molar specific heat of the Einstein model of a monatomic solid

$$C_V = 3R\left(\frac{\theta_E}{T}\right)^2 \cdot \frac{e^{\theta_E/T}}{(e^{\theta_E/T} - 1)^2}. \qquad (49)$$

The (differential) specific heat is a thermodynamic quantity of particular importance since it can be measured directly in calorimetric experiments, and moreover with great accuracy. We note, as foreseen earlier, that on the Einstein model the specific heat should depend only on the single ratio θ_E/T. In other words, if the Einstein model is adequate, it should be possible to "scale" the temperature axis for each substance so that all specific heats of crystalline solids will ideally fall on a single, unique curve when plotted in terms of the "reduced temperature," T/θ_E. Insofar as this procedure is satisfactory, we can then say that the model provides a "law of corresponding states" for the thermal energy and specific heats of crystalline solids.*

In Fig. 7 is reproduced Einstein's original comparison of his theoretical specific heat curve with experimental data on diamond. More detailed comparison of experimental data on various substances with the predictions of the Einstein model shows a number of general features.

(1) The *broad* predictions of the Einstein model are indeed well fulfilled. At sufficiently high temperatures the molar specific heats from experiment are generally found to approach, at least approximately, the classical limiting value of $3R$ (the "Dulong-Petit Law"),

* If the Einstein model were adequate, we should certainly have a law of corresponding states. The converse is not true, however; thus the Debye model (*vide infra*) leads also to a law of corresponding states, although the "Debye characteristic temperature" θ_D that is introduced is naturally not identical with the "Einstein characteristic temperature" θ_E.

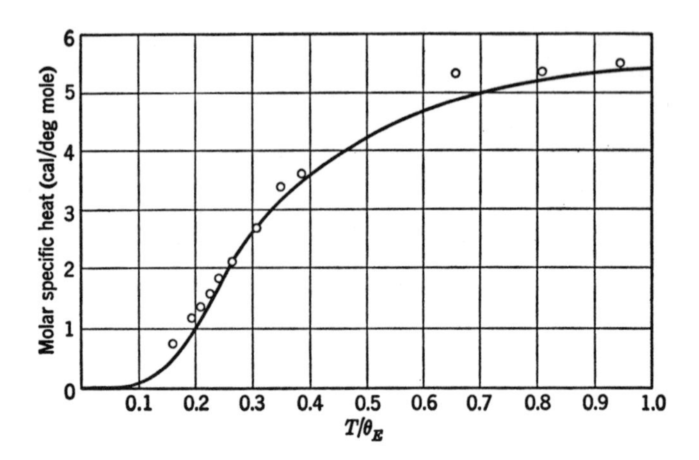

FIG. 7. Molar specific heat of diamond (∘: experimental points) compared with theoretical specific heat curve of Einstein model (full line), taken from Einstein's (1907) original paper.

and at low temperatures the specific heats certainly do begin to decay rapidly and approach zero at very low temperatures.

(2) With some substances we must choose a relatively *low* value of the characteristic temperature θ_E in order for Eq. 49 to fit approximately the appropriate experimental data, whereas in other substances it is necessary to choose quite a *high* value of θ_E. In rough terms substances showing low characteristic temperatures* (e.g., caesium, $\theta \sim 30°K$; lead (Pb), $\theta \sim 90°K$) are materials which we think of as rather soft under normal circumstances, whereas those with very high characteristic temperatures (e.g., diamond, $\theta \sim 2000°K$; beryllium, $\theta \sim 1000°K$) are usually substances which are very hard and/or brittle at normal temperatures. In turn, this means that such hard substances have high frequencies of atomic vibration ($\nu_E = k\theta_E/h$), which is just what we would expect if, other things being equal, the interatomic forces are relatively strong; in other words, we are dealing with materials having high elastic constants.

This general concept of a "characteristic temperature" of a crystalline solid is enormously useful in the physics of the solid state, and the measurement of the specific heat at low temperatures is indeed a very important method for estimating rather directly the characteristic temperature. A similar (though not necessarily identical) charac-

* The characteristic temperatures we quote for caesium and lead are numerically closer to *Debye* characteristic temperatures than to *Einstein* temperatures, but we are concerned here only with approximate comparative values.

teristic temperature enters into the theory of electrical conduction phenomena in metals (cf. Section 2.6); the remarkable feature is just how well a single characteristic temperature will very often suffice for the theoretical description of much of the behavior of a crystalline solid.

(3) The characteristic temperature θ of a solid determines essentially the transition from the so-called quantum region to classical behavior, and we may therefore expect the "reduced temperature" T/θ to give some indication of the magnitude of thermally excited vibrations. We would expect moreover that the amplitude of the thermal vibrations will play an important role in determining the onset of melting and in governing generally the influence of anharmonic effects (see also Sections 2.5 and 4.4). Thus we can expect that the reduced temperature T/θ will be of importance in these matters too—although the precise magnitude of anharmonic effects in a substance will also depend very significantly on the particular type of interatomic potential.

(4) *Detailed* comparison of the specific heat of the Einstein model with experimental data shows progressively greater discrepancies as we go to lower temperatures. James Dewar liquefied hydrogen (boiling point ~20°K) at the Royal Institution, London, in the closing years of the last century, and Kamerlingh Onnes liquefied helium (boiling point ~4°K) in Leiden in 1908. These achievements paved the way for a wide range of experimental work down to very low temperatures, and as early as 1911 Nernst and Lindemann (1911) could say from their experimental results at low temperatures that " . . . der Abfall der Atomwärme bei den untersuchten Elementen Pb, Ag, Zn, Cu, Al und ferner beim KCl bei tiefen Temperaturen *langsamer erfolgt*, als der Formel von Einstein entspricht."*

Despite the progressively more serious failure of the Einstein model at very low temperatures, it remains today a most useful model as a first approach to many problems in solid-state physics.

2.3 THE DEBYE MODEL FOR THE LATTICE VIBRATIONS OF A SOLID

The general thermodynamic problem of dealing adequately with the vibrations of a crystalline solid (the "lattice vibrations") is basically the following. We see first from Eq. 47*c* that the average energy of

* Author's translation: "The decay at low temperatures of the atomic heats [i.e., differential specific heats per mole] of the substances investigated, namely Pb, Ag, Zn, Cu, Al and also KCl, *was slower* than would correspond to Einstein's formula."

an oscillator depends directly on the oscillator frequency ν. This result need not surprise us unduly since the *kinetic* energy of an oscillator will certainly depend on its rate of vibration, and if equipartition of energy is invoked, the *total* energy would simply be twice the kinetic energy. But we have seen that generally (for small vibrations) a stable solid of N particles must be representable by $3N$ independent harmonic oscillators. So to complete the statistical mechanics we must therefore know the distribution in frequency ν of these $3N$ oscillators, for the frequency in turn essentially determines the energy. Now in general we can argue that for a periodic lattice the $3N$ oscillators can be numbered off consecutively, or "counted," quite readily in terms of *wavelength* λ, or equivalently in terms of wave number, or better wave vector $\mathbf{k}$. This is because counting the oscillators (i.e., the independent normal modes of oscillations of the solid) is essentially a matter of fitting the possible wavelengths in an orderly manner to the actual dimensions of the body under consideration.

Thus the problem in the end boils down to determining the relation between wave vector ($\mathbf{k}$) and frequency ν for all the possible normal vibrations of a solid. Physically this means in turn determining the velocity of sound for all possible frequencies, polarizations, and directions of propagation. In general terms this is a far from easy task, and a great deal of work has gone on now for many years toward determining with progressively greater accuracy the vibrational spectrum of crystalline solids [cf., e.g., the textbook by Brillouin, 1946, the classic papers of Born and von Kármán, 1912, 1913, and the more recent work of Blackman (see, e.g., the review by Blackman, 1941)]. Since the end of the Second World War the rapidly increasing availability of electronic computors has made possible great progress in carrying out these rather complex and large-scale computations in considerable detail. We shall not attempt to discuss further the detailed analysis of lattice vibrations for particular types of crystalline solids, but we shall consider a very well-known model due to Debye, a model which illustrates well many of the general principles involved.

Debye in 1912 proposed bold simplifications of the problem, leading to a model which for many purposes reproduces remarkably well the general thermodynamic features of crystalline solids, although more detailed experiments, particularly at low temperatures, reveal considerable discrepancies from the specific predictions of the Debye model. We believe today that very often these discrepancies arise simply and solely because the detailed vibrational spectrum of actual solids is very complex, and in the last analysis each solid must be tackled on its own merits with more or less precision. Debye's model rests on treating the solid concerned as an idealized elastic continuum for the purpose of arriving at a distribution in frequency of the normal modes of vibration.

If we are dealing with low-frequency vibrations of a solid whose wavelength is *long compared with the interatomic spacing*, it must surely be true that for these vibrations we can, with excellent accuracy, treat the solid as an ideal elastic continuum. The differential equation governing a small arbitrary displacement u in such a continuum is

$$\frac{\partial^2 u}{\partial x^2} + \frac{\partial^2 u}{\partial y^2} + \frac{\partial^2 u}{\partial z^2} = \frac{1}{v^2}\frac{\partial^2 u}{\partial t^2}, \tag{50}$$

where v is the velocity of propagation of such a displacement, dependent on the density and elastic constants.* We now seek solutions to this equation where the displacement u will be a simple harmonic function of $\mathbf{r}$ and t; [where $\mathbf{r}$ is the vector (x, y, z)]. For simplicity we assume that we are dealing with a cube of material of side L. We must also impose boundary conditions to select some definite set of possible solutions, and the most convenient is that known as the "Born cyclic condition." This boundary condition means that we are assuming that:

> For each characteristic wave solution (i.e., a normal mode of vibration), the displacement u over the face of the cube $x = 0$ shall always be precisely in phase at all times with the displacement over the face of the cube $x = L$ (and correspondingly for the other faces). (51)

This boundary condition means essentially that the longest wavelength that can be accommodated is L, and that our "normal mode" solutions will correspond to traveling waves (crudely speaking, the wave "disappears" through the cube face at L, "reappearing" simultaneously through the opposite face at 0). An alternative type of boundary condition would involve specifying that the faces of the cube ($x = 0, L$; $y = 0, L$; $z = 0, L$) should always be nodes of vibration; this leads to a "standing wave" type of solution. Apart from the *very* long wavelength solutions (λ comparable in magnitude with L), it is of little consequence physically which particular boundary conditions we adopt in order to pick out a set of normal vibrations. Since in fact the vast majority of normal vibrations have $\lambda \ll L$, we are thus more or less free to make any *convenient* choice of boundary conditions, and the resulting distribution of normal modes of vibration will be

* Moreover, the velocity will also depend specifically on the *type* of displacement (such as shear or dilatation). We shall ignore this sort of complication for the present, however, since in fact the Debye model assumes ultimately that v can be treated as a constant for *all* types of vibration in the solid.

essentially unaffected. We might express this alternatively by saying that only those physical properties which would depend specifically on the actual geometrical boundaries of the solid (i.e., "surface phenomena") could be significantly affected by our particular choice of boundary conditions. Consequently we need not be further concerned when we are dealing with the *bulk* properties of the solid, although in certain specific fields such as catalysis, or more generally in theoretical surface chemistry, we may have to consider very carefully the particular choice of boundary conditions.*

We may then write the desired solutions of Eq. 50 for u in the form:

$$u = A \cos\left(\frac{2\pi \mathfrak{n}_1 x}{L} + \frac{2\pi \mathfrak{n}_2 y}{L} + \frac{2\pi \mathfrak{n}_3 z}{L} - \omega t\right), \tag{52a}$$

where $\omega = 2\pi\nu$; (or alternatively we may write:

$$u = (Rl)\, \mathrm{A} \exp i\, (\mathbf{k} \cdot \mathbf{r} - \omega t), \tag{52b}$$

where $\mathbf{r}$ is the vector $[x, y, z]$, $\mathbf{k}$ is the wave vector $[2\pi\mathfrak{n}_1/L,\ 2\pi\mathfrak{n}_2/L,\ 2\pi\mathfrak{n}_3/L]$, and (Rl) denotes the "real part of"). First, to satisfy the basic differential equation (Eq. 50) requires

$$\mathfrak{n}_1^2 + \mathfrak{n}_2^2 + \mathfrak{n}_3^2 = \frac{\omega^2 L^2}{4\pi^2 v^2}, \tag{53a}$$

where $\mathfrak{n}_1$, $\mathfrak{n}_2$, and $\mathfrak{n}_3$ determine the components of the wave vector $\mathbf{k}$. Alternatively, we may rewrite Eq. 53*a* in terms of an over-all "wave-number," $\mathfrak{n} = (\mathfrak{n}_1^2 + \mathfrak{n}_2^2 + \mathfrak{n}_3^2)^{1/2}$ thus

$$\mathfrak{n} = \pm \frac{\nu L}{v}. \tag{53b}$$

* We should also mention, however, the Born-Raman controversy. It would be fair to say that most workers in lattice dynamics today follow Born and others in assuming that we may number off the lattice vibrations of a solid by imposing some *macroscopic* boundary condition in this way. Raman, however, has always argued that this procedure is only appropriate for the quasi-continuum of relatively long-wave vibrations. If I understand correctly, Raman has maintained that the (certainly very vital) high frequency, short wavelength vibrations are to be regarded as determined by a "boundary condition" essentially imposed by the *unit cell* of the specific lattice concerned. This in turn has led Raman to deduce that the high-frequency spectrum is made up of relatively *few* (perhaps in the order of one or two dozen) sharply discriminated frequencies specifically characteristic of the unit lattice cell. For a further outline of the controversy see, for example, Blackman, 1942; MacDonald, 1952. To quote Raman (1941): "[The vibrations] *of the first class* are on a relatively large scale and may be described without any reference to the fine structure of the solid. These are the elastic vibrations of the crystal . . . [Those] . . . *of the second class* are essentially dependent on the fine structure of the crystal."

We shall not pursue the matter further in this book.

Secondly, to satisfy the boundary conditions (Eq. 51) demands that $\mathfrak{n}_1$, $\mathfrak{n}_2$, and $\mathfrak{n}_3$ must each individually be an integer, i.e.,

$$\mathfrak{n}_1 \quad (\text{and } \mathfrak{n}_2 \text{ and } \mathfrak{n}_3) = \ldots -2, -1, 0, +1, +2, \ldots \qquad (54)$$

To each choice of a triad of (integral) numbers, $\mathfrak{n}_1$, $\mathfrak{n}_2$, $\mathfrak{n}_3$, corresponds then a specific, independent, normal mode of vibration. In fact to each triad there are actually *three* normal modes because, with the Debye model of an isotropic elastic continuum which we are using, the displacement u may be chosen in each case as being *parallel* to the direction of propagation (a longitudinal normal mode), or in the plane perpendicular to the direction of propagation (two independent transverse normal modes). Now the numbers $\mathfrak{n}_1$, $\mathfrak{n}_2$, $\mathfrak{n}_3$ must ultimately run up to very large values (so as to satisfy the requirement that we have $3N$ normal vibrations in all); consequently we are very strongly justified if from now on we regard the numbers $\mathfrak{n}_1$, $\mathfrak{n}_2$, and $\mathfrak{n}_3$ as essentially continuous variables. Thus if small changes $d\mathfrak{n}_1$, $d\mathfrak{n}_2$, $d\mathfrak{n}_3$ are made in these variables, and we bear in mind that unit volume in the space defined by the Cartesian coordinates $\mathfrak{n}_1$, $\mathfrak{n}_2$, $\mathfrak{n}_3$ yields a normal vibration of each polarization (i.e., three normal modes in all), then the corresponding number of independent normal modes of vibrations $d\mathsf{N}$ will be given very closely indeed by

$$d\mathsf{N} = 3d\mathfrak{n}_1 \cdot d\mathfrak{n}_2 \cdot d\mathfrak{n}_3. \qquad (55a)$$

The factor 3 refers of course to the three possible polarizations of a normal mode just mentioned. We can therefore write

$$d\mathsf{N} = 3\mathfrak{n}^2 \, d\mathfrak{n} \sin \theta \, d\theta \, d\phi, \qquad (55b)$$

where $\mathfrak{n}$ is the wave number as defined above preceding Eq. 53*b*, θ is the polar angle which the direction of propagation of a normal mode of vibration makes with the z-axis, and ϕ is the azimuthal angle in the x, y plane. Using Eq. 53*b*, we have

$$d\mathsf{N} = \frac{3\nu^2 L^3}{v^3} \, d\nu \sin \theta \, d\theta \, d\phi, \qquad (55c)$$

assuming boldly that the velocity v is the same for both transverse and longitudinal modes of vibration; or

$$d\tilde{\mathsf{N}} = \frac{3\nu^2}{v^3} \, d\nu \sin \theta \, d\theta \, d\phi, \qquad (55d)$$

where $\tilde{\mathsf{N}}$ refers to the number of normal modes *per unit volume* of the solid. This last result can now be regarded as a fairly general expression for the distribution of normal modes of vibration in terms of the frequency ν and direction of propagation (θ, ϕ), if we regard the velocity v as itself a function of frequency and of the direction of propagation. Following Debye, we now make the sweeping assumption that

(1) The body is entirely isotropic, so that v is *independent* of θ and ϕ. Hence

$$d\tilde{N} = \frac{12\pi}{v^3} \nu^2 \, d\nu. \tag{56}$$

Secondly, Debye also assumed that

(2) The velocity v could be treated as entirely independent of ν (i.e., that the velocity of sound was entirely "nondispersive").

With these assumptions the density of normal modes in frequency $d\tilde{N}/d\nu$ is then directly proportional to ν^2 for all frequencies up to some limiting "cut-off" frequency, say ν_D (the "Debye frequency"), which has to be chosen specifically so that the *total* number of normal modes of vibration per unit volume N is given by

$$\tilde{N} = 3\tilde{N}, \tag{57a}$$

where $\tilde{N}$ is the number of atoms *per unit volume.* Thus from Eq. 56

$$\tilde{N} = \frac{12\pi}{v^3} \int_0^{\nu_D} \nu^2 \, d\nu = 3\tilde{N}. \tag{57b}$$

This in turn immediately determines ν_D as a function of $\tilde{N}$ and v.

$$\nu_D = \left(\frac{3\tilde{N}}{4\pi}\right)^{1/3} v, \tag{57c}$$

and we may eliminate v from Eq. 56 to obtain

$$d\tilde{N} = (9\tilde{N}/\nu_D{}^3)\nu^2 \, d\nu. \tag{56a}$$

The simple Debye distribution in frequency of the normal modes of vibration is shown in Fig. 8*a*; in Fig. 8*b* is sketched a typical (but *fictitious*) frequency distribution for some supposed *real* solid.

The Debye model of the frequency spectrum will in general differ very considerably from that found in real solids (compare again Figs. 8*a* and 8*b*, and we note particularly the single sharp "cut-off" frequency ν_D in the Debye model). However, the prediction that the density of normal modes is proportional to ν^2 is certainly correct *for sufficiently low frequencies* (and hence ultimately for deriving thermodynamic properties *at sufficiently low temperatures*), because we are then concerned with relatively long wavelength vibrations which "see" the solid as a continuum. For these vibrations a ν^2

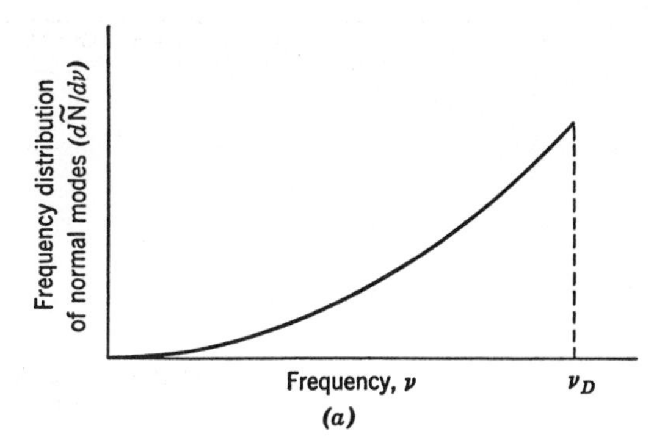

FIG. 8*a*. Sketch of (parabolic) Debye approximation for the frequency distribution of the normal modes of vibration of a crystalline solid.

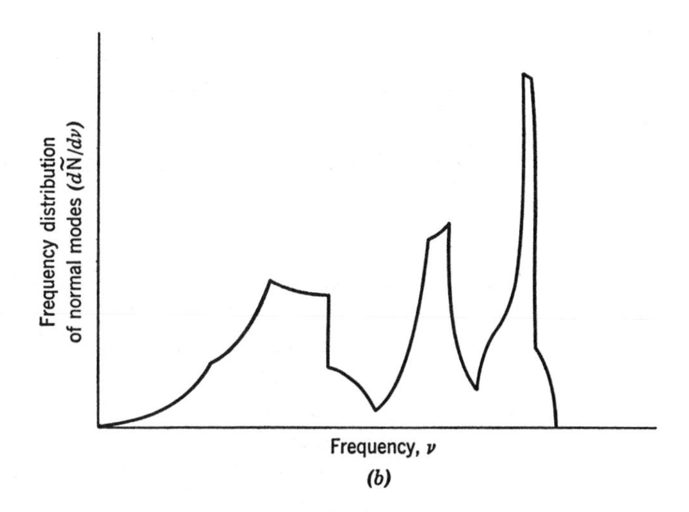

FIG. 8*b*. Sketch of (**fictitious,** but typical) frequency distribution of normal modes of vibration of some supposed physical solid. Fundamental theory regarding the vibrations of regular crystalline solids *in general* predicts that the somewhat surprising "cusps" indicated in the figure must actually occur in the frequency distribution of real solids (cf., e.g., Walker, 1956).

dependence of the frequency spectrum can then be rigorously proved without the sweeping assumptions used previously. The model also satisfies the requirement (as did the Einstein model) of the correct *over-all number* of normal modes of vibration, and hence, as we have also pointed out earlier, the thermodynamic predictions must again

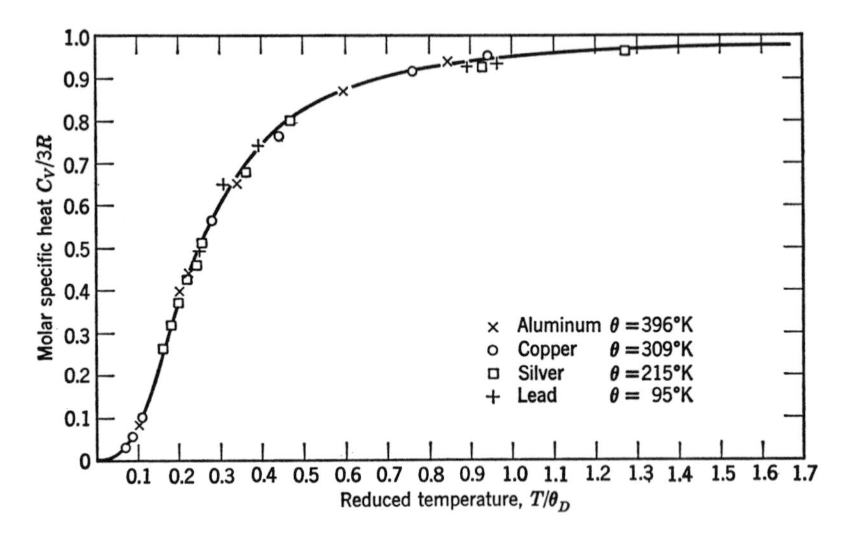

FIG. 9. Experimental data on the specific heat of solids compared with the theoretical specific heat curve (full line) on the Debye model. The experimental data are taken directly from the original paper by Debye (1912).

The values indicated for the Debye characteristic temperature θ are those which yield for each metal the best fit of the experimental points to the theoretical curve.

be correct* at "high" temperatures. Thus since the Debye model must behave correctly at sufficiently low, and at sufficiently high, temperatures it is perhaps natural to expect that it cannot depart too seriously from reality in the intermediate region, and *on the whole* this is more or less true. Figure 9 compares some *experimental* data on the specific heats of various substances with the theoretical predictions of the Debye model, which we develop below; it will be seen that the general agreement is remarkably good.

We should note that the Debye model is often embellished by assuming two different velocities of sound, v_t and v_l, for the transverse and longitudinal modes of vibration respectively (but still assuming both velocities nondispersive and isotropic). This would mean that Eq. 56 should now read

$$d\tilde{N} = 4\pi\left(\frac{2}{v_t^3} + \frac{1}{v_l^3}\right)\nu^2\,d\nu \qquad (56b)$$

with corresponding modifications to subsequent equations. Although

* Remembering always the limitations involved in the assumption of harmonic vibrations.

this sort of extension of the Debye model may seem very reasonable at first sight, it is arguable whether it is really justifiable to make *one* modification of this type, supposedly corresponding more closely to reality, without improving the model in various *other* ways (cf. also Brillouin, 1946, for a fuller discussion of this type of question). We would adopt the point of view that either one adheres to the appealingly simple (but admittedly very approximate) basic Debye model, or else one must tackle the determination of lattice vibration frequencies for individual solids in a much more serious manner.

Using expressions established earlier for harmonic oscillators when dealing with the Einstein model, we can now derive directly the thermodynamic properties of the Debye model. Using Eqs. 45*a* and 56*a*, it follows that the Helmholtz free energy per mole of a monatomic Debye solid will be given by

$$F = \frac{9N\mathcal{V}}{{\nu_D}^3} \int_0^{\nu_D} \langle f(\nu) \rangle \nu^2 \, d\nu, \tag{58a}$$

where $\mathcal{V}$ is the molar volume; therefore

$$F = \tfrac{9}{8}\mathfrak{N}h\nu_D + 9RT\left(\frac{kT}{h\nu_D}\right)^3 \int_0^{h\nu_D/kT} x^2 \cdot \ln\,(1 - e^{-x})\,dx. \tag{58b}$$

Equation 58*b* shows that, on the Debye model, F (and correspondingly the other thermodynamic quantities) can be expressed as a universal function involving a single "characteristic temperature," if we now write

$$h\nu_D = k\theta_D, \tag{59a}$$

thus defining the "Debye characteristic temperature," θ_D, for a solid. Using Eq. 57*c* this means that

$$\theta_D = \frac{h}{k}\left(\frac{3\tilde{N}}{4\pi}\right)^{1/3} v. \tag{59b}$$

Equation 58*b* for F may then be written

$$F = \tfrac{9}{8}R\theta_D - 9RT\left(\frac{T}{\theta_D}\right)^3 \int_0^{\theta_D/T} x^2 \cdot \ln\,[(1 - e^{-x})^{-1}]\,dx. \tag{58c}$$

At sufficiently low temperatures ($T \ll \theta_D$) the second term vanishes (proportionally to T^4), and we are left with the first term, the "zero-point" energy of the solid on the Debye model. On the other hand, at sufficiently high temperatures (strictly speaking $T \gg \theta_D$)

$$F \approx -RT\left(3\ln\frac{T}{\theta_D} + 1 \cdots\right). \tag{58d}$$

We can derive in turn the entropy and the internal energy E in the usual way or, if we prefer, we can proceed more directly to E using Eq. 47c. Thus the molar internal energy is given immediately by

$$E = \frac{9\tilde{N}\mathcal{V}}{\nu_D{}^3} \int_0^{\nu_D} <\epsilon(\nu)> \nu^2 \, d\nu, \tag{60a}$$

where

$$<\epsilon(\nu)> = \frac{h\nu}{2} + \frac{h\nu}{e^{h\nu/kT} - 1}. \tag{47c}$$

Introducing again the "Debye characteristic temperature" θ_D, we have

$$E = \tfrac{9}{8}R\theta_D + 9RT\left(\frac{T}{\theta_D}\right)^3 \int_0^{\theta_D/T} \frac{x^3\, dx}{e^x - 1}. \tag{60b}$$

At sufficiently low temperatures, ($T \ll \theta_D$) the second term tends to zero (proportionally to T^4), leaving us with the first ("zero-point" energy) term; the equality of E and F as $T \to 0$ once again satisfies the general requirements of the Third Law of Thermodynamics. On the other hand, at "high" temperatures (strictly $T \gg \theta_D$), we have

$$E \approx 3RT, \tag{60c}$$

i.e., we meet once more the "classical" result for the internal energy which, we repeat, is a direct consequence of satisfying the purely dynamical requirement of $3N$ independent harmonic oscillators to represent the vibrations of the solid. More generally we can tabulate the second term in Eq. 60b [as a function of the "reduced temperature" (T/θ_D)], and so plot the complete course of E with reduced temperature on the Debye model. However, what is measured *experimentally* is the (differential) specific heat, and it is therefore much more usual to derive the theoretical specific heat at constant volume C_V on the Debye model and then to tabulate this function. We can proceed conveniently from Eq. 60a and we find

$$C_V = \left(\frac{\partial E}{\partial T}\right)_V = 3R \cdot 3\left(\frac{T}{\theta_D}\right)^3 \int_0^{\theta_D/T} \frac{x^4\, dx}{(e^x - 1)(1 - e^{-x})} \tag{61a}$$

$$\equiv 3Rf\left(\frac{T}{\theta_D}\right); \tag{61b}$$

the function $f(T/\theta_D) = C_V/3R$ is plotted in Fig. 10, and a few values are also tabulated in Table 2. At "high" temperatures, $f(T/\theta_D) \to 1$, so that

$$C_V \approx 3R, \tag{61c}$$

which is the "classical" result for the specific heat as we should now

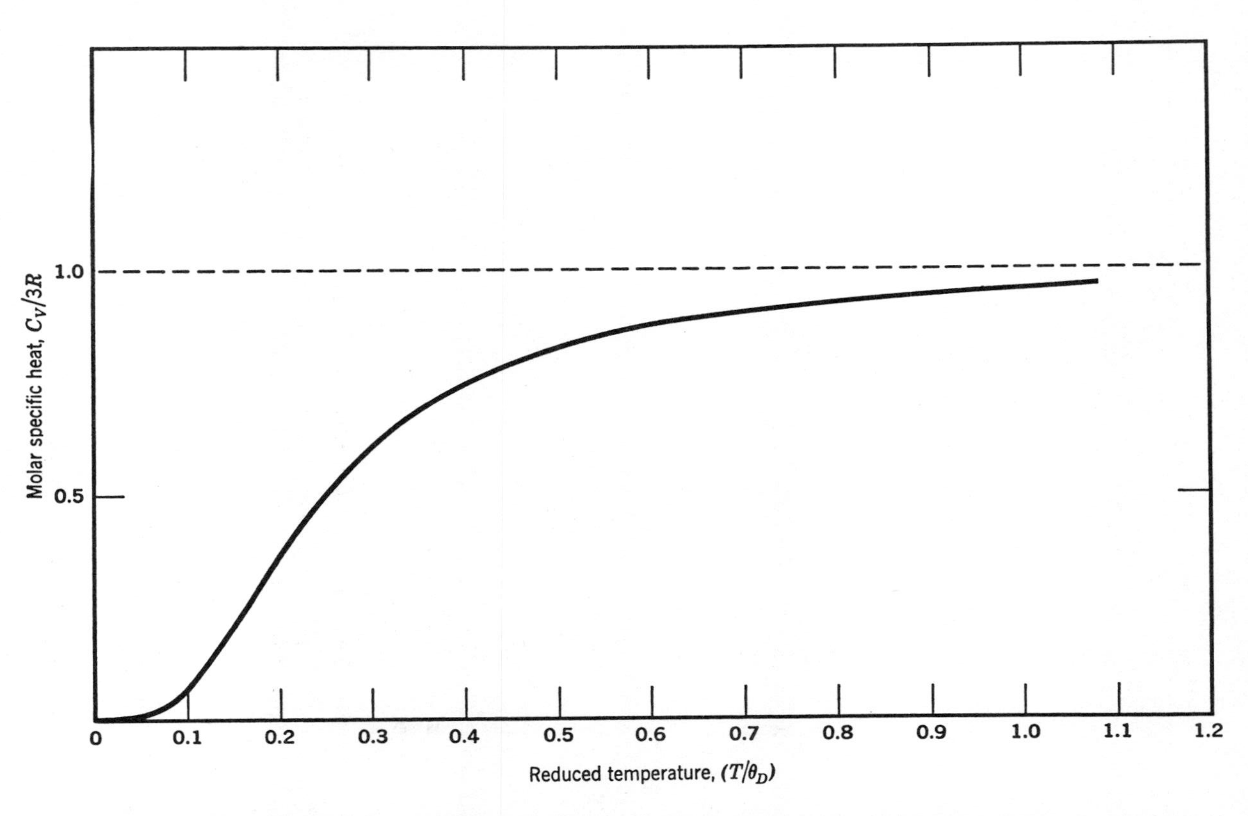

FIG. 10. Theoretical molar specific heat of crystalline solid on the Debye model for the lattice vibrations.

TABLE 2

SHORT TABLE OF DEBYE SPECIFIC HEAT FUNCTION

T/θ_D	$C_V/3R$
<0.04	$77.927(T/\theta_D)^3$
0.05	0.00974
0.075	0.0328
0.1	0.0758
0.15	0.213
0.2	0.3686
0.333	0.6628
0.5	0.8254
0.667	0.8960
1.0	0.9517
2.0	0.9876
5.0	0.9980
∞	1.0000

Derived from data of J. A. Beattie, 1926, as reproduced by Fowler and Guggenheim (1939).

expect (within the harmonic approximation). On the other hand, at very low temperatures ($T \ll \theta_D$),

$$f\left(\frac{T}{\theta_D}\right) \approx 3\left(\frac{T}{\theta_D}\right)^3 \int_0^\infty \frac{x^4\,dx}{(e^x - 1)(1 - e^{-x})};$$

the integral has the value $4\pi^4/15$ and hence

$$\frac{C_V}{3R} \approx \frac{4\pi^4}{5}\left(\frac{T}{\theta_D}\right)^3, = 77.9_3\left(\frac{T}{\theta_D}\right)^3. \tag{61d}$$

Equation 61*d* then embodies the renowned "Debye T^3-Law" for the lattice specific heat of a solid at sufficiently low temperatures. A general comparison has been made (Fig. 9) of experimental specific heat data with the predictions of the Debye model. On the whole the agreement is remarkably good, and the Debye model therefore remains today an extremely useful approximation for the analysis of the lattice vibrations of a solid.

2.4 COMMENT ON THE ANALYSIS

When first discussing the "micro-states" of the crystalline solid, we assumed that we were dealing with an assembly of lattice points distinguished from one another by their location in (real) *space* and that an independent "label" of some sort could be attached to each of these sites specifying the particular state of the atom or molecule at that site. Thus in the simplest case, as we pointed out, the configuration

$$\begin{matrix} H\ H\ H\ T\ \ldots \\ T\ H\ H\ T\ \ldots \\ \ldots\ldots\ldots \end{matrix} \qquad (H = \text{"heads,"}\ T = \text{"tails"!})$$

is treated as a distinguishable configuration from, say,

$$\begin{matrix} T\ H\ T\ H\ \ldots \\ H\ H\ H\ T\ \ldots \\ \ldots\ldots\ldots \end{matrix}$$

although the number of individual H and T configurations is the same in the two situations as illustrated. In such cases the model we are using is that of "independent localized elements." It may bear emphasizing that it is not being said that a solid body (and in particular a *crystalline* solid) *is* necessarily an assembly of independent localized elements; this is simply being proposed as an idealized model, and indeed it is one limiting, and very useful, model with which statistical mechanics can deal straightforwardly.

By the time we arrive at the Debye model the situation has obviously changed considerably, and in brief our model now is really one of "independent oscillators localized in *wave vector space*," rather than "independent elements localized in real space." The important thing, however, is that although the atomic sites in the idealized crystalline solid were distinguishable by their space coordinates, whether or not they bore the same "label" (generally speaking, an energy state ϵ_i), similarly, since no two Debye oscillators representing a crystalline solid can strictly have *identical* wave vectors $[\mathfrak{n}_1, \mathfrak{n}_2, \mathfrak{n}_3]$, the Debye oscillators are "distinguishable" whether they bear essentially the same energy label or not.

The point of our discussion is that, in contrast, when we turn to the other limiting type of model with which we shall deal (essentially the idealized gas model, see Chapter 3), the elements have then *no* distinguishing "mark" other than the energy label which determines essentially the state they are occupying. Then we say that we are dealing with a model of "independent, nonlocalized elements." The snag in nature is that very many interesting substances, and particularly liquids, cannot be regarded as conforming particularly closely to *either* of these two limiting models with which we can deal readily.

2.5 SOME REMARKS ON ANHARMONICITY

2.5.1 The Quasi-harmonic Model

The Einstein and Debye models are restricted to assemblies of harmonic oscillators as we have seen, and therefore *strictly speaking* we should not attempt with such models to deal with properties of solids which arise primarily as a very consequence of anharmonicity of lattice vibrations. Thus consider a fictitious assembly of atoms, each of which could make localized and strictly harmonic vibrations about its own position of equilibrium. If such an assembly is "heated up," the atomic vibrations will increase in amplitude, but, more or less obviously by symmetry, the mean position of each atom will remain unchanged **so long as the individual atomic vibrations remain precisely harmonic** and hence no thermal expansion would result.* This in turn means that there should be no difference, for example, between C_p and C_V for such an assembly. So, to be perfectly consistent, a model based on an assembly of strictly harmonic oscillators should not be used to discuss possible anharmonic effects.

However, one can make some useful progress following the lead of Born and Grüneisen by assuming effectively that

(1) The anharmonicity, when significant, causes the atoms to take up new average positions of equilibrium (dependent now on the amplitude of the vibrations, and hence on the temperature), but that

(2) The vibrations about the *new* positions of dynamic equilibrium remain closely harmonic. This is at least a very appealing assumption whose consequences we shall now pursue; we shall indicate later in Section 4.4 how a more detailed statistical mechanical analysis can proceed on a simple atomic model involving a specific anharmonic potential.

2.5.2 The Grüneisen Parameter and Grüneisen's Equation

Let us consider then a crystalline solid whose thermodynamic properties can be defined by a single characteristic temperature θ (e.g., the Debye model where $\theta = \theta_D$). We also assume that *at any*

* If we are dealing with a *real* three-dimensional solid, the coupling of the motion of one atom with that of its neighbors makes the definition of a real "harmonic" solid rather difficult and the detailed analysis far from easy. Thus, for example, Barron (1957) points out that even a particularly simple two-dimensional assembly of "atoms," each coupled to neighbors by forces which are *individually* harmonic along the line of centers, will nonetheless provide a model which, far from expanding, would contract with increasing amplitude of vibration!

given volume V the harmonic approximation is adequate, so that the characteristic frequency (ν_D in the Debye model), and hence the characteristic temperature θ, are *not* explicit functions of the absolute temperature T. We further assume, as did Grüneisen, that a change of volume V can be adequately described by a change in θ; i.e., $\theta = \theta(V)$. Thus, if the Debye model were a good approximation to start with, one would be assuming that under external pressure another Debye spectrum would be an equally good approximation; or, in other words, that the frequency of each normal mode of vibration is changed in simple proportion as the volume is changed. The important thing is to realize that these *are* assumptions, which are extremely useful as first approximations, but which must be examined critically if we wish to consider a more detailed lattice-dynamical model.

With our assumptions, we can then write for the entropy

$$S = S\left(\frac{T}{\theta}\right), \tag{62}$$

and $\theta = \theta(V)$. Hence

$$\left(\frac{\partial S}{\partial V}\right)_T = -S' \cdot \frac{T}{\theta^2}\frac{\partial \theta}{\partial V} = \frac{S'}{V} \cdot \frac{T}{\theta}\gamma, \tag{62a}$$

where S' means differentiation with respect to the reduced temperature T/θ as variable and

$$\gamma \equiv -\frac{d \ln \theta}{d \ln V}. \tag{63}$$

The parameter γ expresses in a dimensionless form the relative change of θ with volume, and is defined with a negative sign because normally speaking we would expect the frequency of atomic vibrations (and hence θ) to increase under pressure, i.e., to increase with reduction of volume V; hence γ as defined is normally positive and moreover is normally of order of magnitude unity. On an idealized model, θ will only change with volume if the lattice potential is to some degree anharmonic, and consequently γ is a measure of anharmonicity. Now we have also from Eq. 62

$$\left(\frac{\partial S}{\partial T}\right)_V = \frac{S'}{\theta}, \tag{64}$$

and thus

$$C_V = T\left(\frac{\partial S}{\partial T}\right)_V = \frac{T}{\theta}S'. \tag{64a}$$

Now by one of Maxwell's thermodynamic relations

$$\left(\frac{\partial S}{\partial V}\right)_T = \left(\frac{\partial p}{\partial T}\right)_V = -\frac{1}{V}\left(\frac{\partial V}{\partial T}\right) \Big/ \frac{1}{V}\left(\frac{\partial V}{\partial p}\right)_T \equiv \frac{\beta}{\chi_T}, \qquad (62b)$$

where β denotes the coefficient of thermal expansion and χ_T the isothermal compressibility. Hence comparing Eqs. 62a and 62b with Eq. 64a, we have immediately

$$\frac{\beta}{\chi_T} = \frac{\gamma}{V} C_V, \qquad (65a)$$

i.e.,

$$\beta = \frac{\gamma \chi_T C_V}{V}. \qquad (65b)$$

(Alternatively, we can express β in terms of C_p and the *adiabatic* (isentropic) compressibility, χ_S, which are usually more easily measured than C_V and χ_T; using the standard thermodynamic relation $(C_p/C_V) = (\chi_T/\chi_S)$, we have

$$\beta = \frac{\gamma \chi_S C_p}{V}. \qquad (65c)$$

If C_V and C_p are molar specific heats, V in the denominator of Eqs. 65b and 65c will be the corresponding molar volume; alternatively, we can simply write

$$\beta = \gamma \chi_T c_V, = \gamma \chi_S c_p, \qquad (65d)$$

where c_V and c_p are specific heats, *per unit volume*.)

We can look at the Grüneisen equation (Eq. 65b) in a number of ways.

(1) First, it predicts indeed that thermal expansion (β) will only arise as a consequence of anharmonicity through the parameter γ.

(2) Secondly, assuming that γ is itself independent of temperature (as it should be in terms of the model) and that we can ignore also any explicit temperature-dependence of the compressibility χ_T then the thermal expansion coefficient β should be directly proportional to the specific heat C_V in its detailed temperature dependence. Thus, since at "high" temperatures C_V should be constant (classical behavior), correspondingly the thermal expansion coefficient β should also be a constant, and at sufficiently *low* temperatures β should tend to zero proportionally to T^3.

Broadly speaking, these predictions about the behavior of β are quite well borne out experimentally in typical substances, although in detail many discrepancies are found. The predicted vanishing of the thermal

TABLE 3

VALUES OF THE GRÜNEISEN PARAMETER γ FOR SOME METALS AS DERIVED FROM DATA ON THERMAL EXPANSION, SPECIFIC HEAT, AND COMPRESSIBILITY; AS GIVEN BY MOTT AND JONES (1936)

Element	γ
[Alkali (Group IA) metals]	
Li	1.17
Na	1.25
K	1.34
Rb	1.48
Cs	1.29
(Group IB metals)	
Cu	1.96
Ag	2.40
Au	3.03
(Some other metals)	
Mg	1.51
Al	2.17
Cd	2.19
Sb	0.92
W	1.75
Pt	2.54

expansion as we approach the absolute zero is again in accordance with the principles of the Third Law of Thermodynamics.

(3) Using measured values of the thermal expansion, of the specific heat, and of the compressibility, we can derive from Eq. 65*b* (or 65*c*) a value for the parameter γ which may itself be of value in estimating the influence of anharmonicity on *other* thermal parameters (such as the electrical resistivity of a metal, *vide infra*). Values of γ derived in this way are given in Table 3.

2.6 ELECTRICAL RESISTIVITY OF METALS

2.6.1 DEPENDENCE ON TEMPERATURE AND VOLUME

Strictly speaking the electrical (or thermal) resistivity of conducting solids are not integral parts of statistical mechanics since they are not equilibrium phenomena. However, statistical mechanics is a vital tool in the general field of electronic properties, and therefore it will not be amiss perhaps to outline how a simple model of the electrical resistivity in a good conductor may be set up and then used to discuss broadly certain important features.

The electrical conduction in a solid will be governed basically in two ways: first, by the number of electrons *available* for conduction at any given temperature, and secondly, by the ease or otherwise with which these electrons can be transported through the conductor under the influence of an electric field (determining the electrical conductivity) or when attempting to diffuse under an imposed temperature gradient (determining in turn the thermal conductivity). In a "good" (metallic) conductor the effective number of electrons available for conduction is comparable with the number of atoms in the solid, and moreover the number does not change significantly with temperature; therefore we need only concern ourselves directly with the freedom of movement of the electrons (crudely speaking, their "viscosity") in moving through the lattice.

Now a general theorem tells us that only the *thermal* vibrations of an otherwise perfect and homogeneous lattice (i.e., without chemical or physical imperfections) can "scatter" the conduction electrons.* We therefore expect that the electrical resistivity is going to depend in some way or another on the displacement of the lattice atoms arising from thermal vibrations. It is generally assumed that the electron scattering which leads to resistivity is a small perturbation on the electronic behavior, and we might therefore assume brashly that the resistivity could be expressed as a power series in the atomic displacements. Assuming moreover that no linear term in the atomic displacement will occur (because we should otherwise have to include a modulus sign, which is analytically undesirable), we would then on this very crude argument expect the resistivity ρ to depend in first approximation on the mean square amplitude of atomic vibrations.

In a simple harmonic oscillator of displacement x, frequency ν, and mass m, the average potential energy is $2m\pi^2\nu^2 \langle x^2 \rangle$, and in a steady state we would expect $2m\pi^2\nu^2 \langle x^2 \rangle = \langle \epsilon \rangle /2$, where $\langle \epsilon \rangle$ is the average total energy of the oscillator. Thus if we assume, as we discussed, that $\rho \propto \langle x^2 \rangle$, we should expect $\rho \propto \langle \epsilon \rangle / m\nu^2$, i.e.,

$$\rho = \frac{\tilde{C} \langle \epsilon \rangle}{m\nu^2}, \tag{66a}$$

where $\tilde{C}$ is some constant involving the magnitude of the scattering

* In other words, the zero-point energy (or zero-point vibrations) of the lattice does not scatter the conduction electrons. To the physicists this is usually known as "Bloch's theorem," to mathematicians it involves "Floquet's theorem."

interaction between the vibrating lattice and the conduction electrons. Assuming that we may write at normal temperatures $<\epsilon> = kT$ and introduce a characteristic temperature θ for the lattice, proportional to ν, we have then

$$\rho = \frac{CT}{M\theta^2}, \tag{66b}$$

where C is another constant (proportional to $\tilde{C}$) and M is the molar mass. This is indeed a very convenient expression for discussing the general behavior of the electrical resistivity of metals at not too low temperatures. We see immediately the explicit linear dependence of ρ on T, and we can use Eq. 66*b* to give us some idea of how resistance will vary with volume and in the melting process.

From Eq. 66*b*, if we assume that C does not vary with volume, we have

$$\left(\frac{\partial \ln \rho}{\partial \ln V}\right)_T = -2\frac{\partial \ln \theta}{\partial \ln V} = 2\gamma, \tag{67}$$

where γ is the Grüneisen parameter introduced previously (Section 2.5.2). Table 4 gives some experimental data on the change of resistivity with volume as compared with values of 2γ, and we see that there is some moderate agreement. There is in fact no strong justification for assuming that the interaction constant C would actually be independent of volume, and therefore we cannot really expect any detailed quantitative agreement, quite apart from any other limitations of the general model discussed.

If we make measurements of resistivity ρ at constant volume, Eq. 66*b* suggests that ρ should vary linearly with T; however, it is much more straightforward experimentally to measure the variation of ρ with T at more or less constant pressure (usually atmospheric pressure). We can then estimate from Eq. 66*b* what difference we may expect on our assumptions between measurements of ρ at constant pressure and at constant volume. We have for the total change of resistance with temperature

$$\frac{d \ln \rho}{d \ln T} = \left(\frac{\partial \ln \rho}{\partial \ln T}\right)_V + \left(\frac{\partial \ln \rho}{\partial \ln V}\right)_T \left(\frac{\partial \ln V}{\partial \ln T}\right)_p, \tag{68a}$$

and if we use Eq. 66*b* and assume again that C is independent of volume, we have

$$\frac{d \ln \rho}{d \ln T} = 1 - 2\frac{\partial \ln \theta}{\partial \ln V}\beta T = 1 + 2\beta\gamma T. \tag{68b}$$

TABLE 4

COMPARISON OF EXPERIMENTAL DATA ON *VOLUME* DEPENDENCE OF RESISTIVITY WITH GRÜNEISEN ANHARMONICITY PARAMETER, γ

Metal	$\left(\frac{\partial \ln \rho}{\partial \ln V}\right)_T$ * From Experiment	2γ †
(Alkali metals)		
Li	−0.5	2.34
Na	+4.5	2.50
K	+4.2	2.68
Rb	+2.95	2.96
(Group IB metals)		
Cu	2.7	3.92
Ag	3.6	4.80
Au	5.2	6.06
(Some other metals)		
Al	2.9	4.34
W	4.3	3.24
Pt	5.6	5.08

* The values for the alkali metals are determined from Bridgman's work, as quoted by MacDonald and Pearson (1953); the values for the remaining metals are taken from Mott and Jones (1936).

† After Mott and Jones (1936).

The second term on the right-hand side of Eq. 68*b* then accounts on our model for the difference between measurements of the dependence of ρ on T at constant pressure and at constant volume, and we see that this again involves directly the Grüneisen anharmonicity parameter, γ.

Equation 68*b* is also useful in suggesting that the relative influence of lattice anharmonic effects in temperature may be expected, as a first approximation, to involve rather generally the factor $\beta\gamma T$. This dimensionless factor may be written formally as a "reduced (anharmonic) temperature" T/T_{anh}, where

$$T_{\text{anh}} \equiv (\beta\gamma)^{-1}. \tag{69}$$

This "anharmonicity temperature" T_{anh} would then be some measure of a temperature at which anharmonic effects would be expected to become *entirely dominant* or, in other words, where the harmonic approximation would have broken down entirely. So long as $T/T_{anh} \ll 1$, one might assume that anharmonic effects would be a fairly small perturbation and consequently one might feel reasonably justified in using the "quasi-harmonic" model in the way we have outlined. Since γ is typically of order unity, and β in metals is of order 10^{-4} to 10^{-5}/deg, we would expect to satisfy the requirement $T/T_{anh} \ll 1$ rather generally so long as T did not exceed typically a few hundred degrees Kelvin.

2.6.2 Change of Resistivity on Melting

To estimate how the electrical resistivity of a metal should change on melting requires, naturally enough, some assumptions about the liquid state. Simon (1924) made the *ad hoc* (but not unreasonable) assumption that we might relate the resistivity in a metal rather generally to the lattice entropy S. Now the entropy of a crystalline solid at normal temperatures is of magnitude R (cf., e.g., Eq. 46*b*), and the discontinuous entropy *increase* on melting is also generally of order R (cf., e.g., Mott and Jones, 1936, p. 278). Thus on Simon's general hypothesis we might expect (so long as the number of free electrons available for conduction does not change markedly on melting) that the resistance would *increase* discontinuously at the melting point and typically we might expect something like a doubling of the resistance. Table 5 (taken from Mott and Jones, 1936) indicates the general qualitative success of this hypothesis, and it is certainly useful to bear in mind that there should be a broad connection between the electrical resistivity and the "degree of disorder" of the lattice. However, we see that the connection cannot be very direct since at "high" temperatures we have a dominant term in S increasing *logarithmically* with T (see again, e.g., Eq. 46*b*), whereas it is certainly true that a *linear* increase of ρ with T, as predicted by Eq. 66*b*, is generally much closer to the mark.

Mott (1934) assumed in essence that the resistivity change on melting arose primarily from the change in frequency of atomic vibrations; in other words Mott assumed that we could effectively ignore the spatial disordering of the atoms in the liquid when calculating the resistivity ρ. This picture could obviously be regarded as leading to one limiting model for a liquid; in the past it was felt that there was some justification for such a model from X-ray studies, since these appeared

TABLE 5

EXPERIMENTAL DATA ON INCREASE OF RESISTANCE OF METALS ON MELTING (AFTER MOTT AND JONES, 1936)

	Metal	Resistance of Liquid / Resistance of Solid (at melting point)
(Alkali metals)		
	Li	1.68
	Na	1.45
	K	1.55
	Rb	1.61
	Cs	1.66
(Group IB metals)		
	Cu	2.1
	Ag	1.9
	Au	2.3
(Some other metals)		
	Al	1.64
	Cd	2.1
	*Sb	0.67*

* NOTE: Sb is one of three metallic elements (Sb, Ga, Bi) whose resistance *diminishes* on melting; of these elements two (Ga, Bi) also *contract* on melting. It is believed that, broadly speaking, the resistance *decrease* is related to the fact that in these particular metals the general structure of the matrix becomes much more isotropic when molten.

to indicate very considerable short-range order among the atoms in the liquid. Today, however, the interpretation appears rather less certain, and the recent work of Bernal (e.g., 1959) argues that in fact the spatial arrangement of atoms in a liquid is, on the whole, about as random as possible, consistent with packing together the atoms to the required volume of the liquid.

The general situation is developing quite rapidly at the moment (1962), and it seems certain that our understanding of liquids will progress considerably within the next few years. Be that as it may, let us use Mott's hypothesis together with Eq. 66*b* to see how we may estimate on that basis the resistance change in a metal on melting. In general, the volume of the liquid is greater than that of the solid; consequently the interatomic distance increases, and we would therefore expect that θ would diminish. Physically this means of course that at a given temperature the amplitude of atomic vibrations increases, and so ρ increases, on our previous assumption that $\rho \propto \langle x^2 \rangle$. Very crudely from Eq. 63 we might then write

$$\frac{\Delta\theta}{\theta} \approx -\gamma \frac{\Delta V}{V}, \tag{70}$$

where ΔV is the volume change on melting. From Eq. 66*b* we also have crudely

$$\frac{\Delta\rho}{\rho} \approx -2 \frac{\Delta\theta}{\theta}, \tag{71}$$

if again we assume that C does not change significantly on melting. Hence we might write

$$\frac{\Delta\rho}{\rho} \approx 2\gamma \frac{\Delta V}{V}, \tag{72}$$

as a *very* rough approximation. A relative volume increase of the order of 10%, and a typical γ of about 2, would then predict very roughly a relative resistivity increase of about 50%, which at least is of the right sort of magnitude. The model demands much more careful analysis than we have suggested, but at least these discussions should indicate how the "quasi-harmonic model" using Grüneisen's parameter can be of great value in discussing a wide range of phenomena.

2.6.3 Resistivity at Very Low Temperatures

Finally, we might make a guess at how we would expect the electrical resistivity of a metal arising from thermal vibrations to vary at very low temperatures ($T \ll \theta$). Using the Debye model for the lattice vibrations, we might boldly suggest that we should replace Eq. 66*b* more generally by

$$\rho = \frac{CT}{M\theta^2}\, g\left(\frac{T}{\theta}\right), \tag{73}$$

where

$$g\left(\frac{T}{\theta}\right) = 3\left(\frac{T}{\theta}\right)^3 \int_0^{\theta/T} \frac{x^3\,dx}{e^x - 1}, \tag{73a}$$

the function $g(T/\theta)$ being taken directly from the expression for the thermally excited energy of a Debye solid (second term on right-hand side of Eq. 60*b*). We do *not* include in Eqs. 73 and 73*a* any contribution from the zero-point energy term because, as we remarked earlier, a general theorem tells us that the zero-point vibrations of a solid do not of themselves contribute to the electrical resistivity. The function $g(T/\theta)$ tends to unity at "high" temperatures, reproducing Eq. 66*b*, whereas at very low temperatures ($T \ll \theta$) Eq. 73 would predict that the resistance would decay as $T^4/M\theta^5$. The detailed theory of electrical resistivity arising from lattice thermal vibrations yields somewhat more complex, but qualitatively rather similar, expressions; in particular, the so-called Bloch-Grüneisen theory leads to

$$\rho = \frac{CT^5}{M\theta^6} 4 \int_0^{\theta/T} \frac{x^5\,dx}{(e^x - 1)(1 - e^{-x})}, \tag{74}$$

which predicts that ρ will decay as $T^5/M\theta^6$ at low temperatures. The general theory of electrical resistivity is rather complicated (e.g., Mott and Jones, 1936; Wilson, 1953; Ziman, 1960), but Eq. 73 can at least give a useful *qualitative* picture of how the resistivity of a metal should vary with temperature.

This completes our main discussion of the statistical mechanics of crystalline solids; we now focus our attention on the other extreme, that of idealized "gaslike" models. This will enable us in turn to consider other fundamental problems such as the statistics of electrons in metals and the intensity of electromagnetic radiation, as well as, of course, the immediate problem of real gases themselves.

3

GASLIKE ASSEMBLIES

3.1 INTRODUCTION

So far we have been concerned with the statistical mechanics of solids, and more particularly of crystalline solids. The primary model for a solid involved us in the concept of strictly localized "elements" (atoms or molecules) or, more properly, of strictly localized (energy) states occupied by these "elements."* When considering gases, or more generally "gaslike" problems, we meet the opposite extreme for our model. We assume now that our atoms, or molecules, can occupy energy states which are determined primarily by the macroscopic, over-all, geometrical boundaries of the "container,"† and that these states are entirely nonlocalized within the interior of the container. The physical dimensions of a macroscopic container are, of course, extremely large compared with *atomic* dimensions, and it turns out that these individual permissible energy states, ϵ_r say, in such a gas model are then extremely closely spaced in energy. Because we assume that the states are now entirely nonlocalized, all that is necessary, or indeed permissible, to define a distinguishable "microscopic" configuration, or complexion, of the gas is to specify which of these energy levels are occupied and by how many particles. This specifi-

* Subsequently, of course, this developed into a model of coupled vibrations where the independent "elements" were then independent "Debye oscillators" rather than independent *atoms*, and the oscillators were then localized or distinguishable in "wave-vector space" rather than in *real* space.

† If we are dealing with a real gas, the container will be some actual, physical, empty box or some such object for containing the gas in the familiar and obvious sense. If we are considering instead the free electrons in a metal as an "electron-gas," the metal itself will be the "container" (*vide infra*).

cation of an individual complexion of the assembly then embodies the very essentials of an assembly of "nonlocalized" elements. If moreover we assume, as we shall, that the occupation of any one particular molecular or atomic energy level is *a priori* independent of the occupation of any other energy level, we may say that we are dealing with an assembly of "nonlocalizable independent elements."

Let us now emphasize that we are *not* stating that any particular gas *is* made up of particles which are entirely "nonlocalizable" and entirely independent. The point, once again, is that this model lends itself readily to statistical mechanical analysis and appears to be reasonably adequate for the discussion of a number of physical problems, just as the model of strictly localized, independent, elements was reasonably adequate for the discussion of many solid state questions. What is then clear, however, is that the real, physical, liquid state presents very serious difficulties for statistical mechanics because, rather obviously, the atoms are neither in strictly localizable states (after all they do move around!) nor are they anywhere near the limit of complete "nonlocalizability." This suggests why many attempts have been made *either* to treat the liquid state on some sort of quasi-crystalline picture (so that we may start from a "localized" model) but with the somewhat *ad hoc* addition of a number of "vacancies" to provide in some way for the mobility of a liquid, *or* alternatively, to try to treat the liquid as a rather dense "gas," essentially because we can then make a start from the standpoint of "nonlocalizable" elements in an assembly. These models for the liquid state have had varying degrees of success, and the statistical mechanics of liquids offers a challenging field of research. We shall not, however, attempt here to discuss further these models. In any case one would think that such approaches to the analysis of the liquid state, either from the starting point essentially of a crystalline solid model or of a gas model, must surely remain arbitrary to some extent because, to misquote Gertrude Stein (1922), "A liquid is a liquid is a liquid is a liquid is a liquid is a liquid . . . ." The only problem in liquids which we shall discuss in any detail is the direct application of Bose-Einstein statistics for the ideal noninteracting gas model to the case of liquid helium II (i.e., liquid He^4 below the "lambda-point"—i.e., below 2.19°K under its saturated vapor pressure). This is certainly a very bold application of statistical mechanics to a liquid; it was first made in 1938 by the late F. London. This use of "ideal gas" statistics for dealing with a liquid is perhaps somewhat less surprising if we bear in mind that liquid helium is a very unusual liquid which, at least on the face of it, might be regarded as more "gaslike" than other liquids, particularly when we recall its very low density.

This whole position is mirrored by the general situation in physics that our detailed understanding of the liquid state is much more meager than that of the crystalline solid or of the gas. There are well-established fields of specialization at the two extremes: "solid state physics" and "gas physics," but nothing really comparable exists yet as a systematic and coherent body of knowledge for "liquid state physics." Another way of looking at the question is to notice that in the crystalline solid we are dealing primarily with a highly *ordered*, and very regular, array of atoms or molecules, whereas in a tenuous gas we have, in direct contrast, an assembly of elements whose spatial distribution is highly *disordered.* The liquid provokes particular difficulties because neither of these limits is really applicable. One might perhaps guess that it will be from the study of liquids proper that major new developments in statistical mechanics will ultimately come.

3.2 THE ANALYSIS OF THE GASEOUS MODEL

In general, as we have said, in a "gaslike" assembly the individual permissible energy states (say ϵ_r, ϵ_s, ϵ_t, . . . , etc.) are enormous in number or in other words *extremely* closely spaced in energy.* We are therefore quite justified (and our analysis is simplified) if we "lump together" groups of many states closely neighboring in energy, assuming that in each of these groups the variation of energy (ϵ) from state to state is quite negligible, but, on the other hand, supposing that the over-all occupation number in any group is sufficiently *large* that convenient statistical approximations are adequate.† We therefore assume that we have chosen successive groups of energy levels in this way (see Fig. 11) so that in the ith group there are altogether ω_i distinct elementary states occupied in all by n_i elements or "particles," and we assume that the states in this group are so close together in energy that they may be taken as having the *same* energy ϵ_i; similarly for the jth group, etc. The *precise* choice of ω_i, ω_j, etc., that we envisage is of no ultimate consequence; all that matters is that we are entitled to consider together, as we have said, sufficient permissible levels in each group to make our statistical analysis of the behavior

* We should also note that for all but the *very* lowest energy levels the degeneracy of an *individual* energy-level will be very high in a gaslike assembly.

† Let us state rather arbitrarily, but categorically, that for all real gases, and for assemblies obeying Fermi-Dirac statistics, this approach is quite warranted (see also the preceding footnote). The only situation where one may have to be prepared to cavil is in the so-called "Bose-Einstein condensation phenomenon." We shall refer to this again later in this chapter.

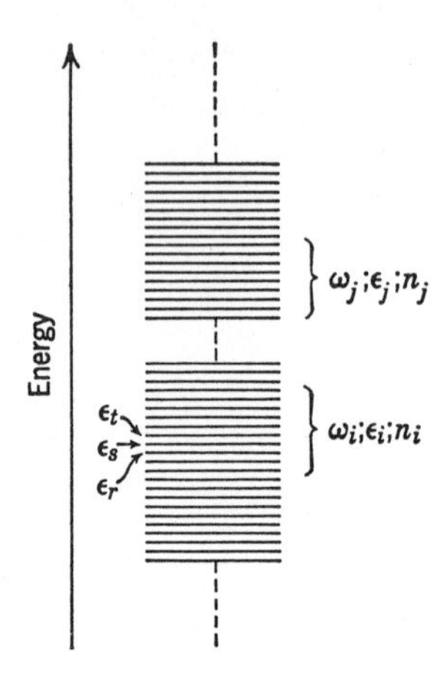

FIG. 11. Sketch to illustrate the very closely spaced *individual* energy levels (e.g., ϵ_r, ϵ_s, ϵ_t, . . .), in a gas model, and the grouping of these levels together for analysis purposes. Thus in the ith group we suppose that these are altogether ω_i individual "elementary" states, all having essentially the *same* energy ϵ_i. The number of elementary states in each group is presumed always to be sufficiently large that the probable occupation number for the whole group (e.g., in the ith group) is also large; i.e., $n_i \gg 1$ for the ith group.

of a group straightforward. Finally then the *total* number of elements N in the *whole* assembly will be given by

$$N = \sum_i n_i, \qquad \text{(cf. Eq. 16}a\text{)}, \quad (75a)$$

and the *total* energy E of the whole assembly by

$$E = \sum_i n_i \epsilon_i, \qquad \text{(cf. Eq. 16}b\text{)}. \quad (75b)$$

Now we consider the behavior of one of the groups (say the ith), which could be called a "subensemble," or "subassembly." We then ask in how many different configurations we may fill this ith group with n_i particles. There is no energy restriction to worry us here since we have assumed that all the levels in this group have the *same* energy (ϵ_i). If, further, there is no restriction on how many of these n_i particles may occupy any *single* state in the group, then the total number of distinguishable configurations in the ith group, say Ω_i, is given (exactly) by

$$\Omega_i = \frac{(\omega_i + n_i - 1)!}{(\omega_i - 1)!n_i!},$$

(see Appendix III). (76)

Consequently the number of distinguishable configurations for the *whole* assembly of independent elements, when we have n_1 particles in the first group, n_2 in the second, n_i in the ith group, n_j in the jth group, etc., is given by

$$\tilde{\Omega} = \Omega_1\Omega_2 \cdots \Omega_i\Omega_j \cdots = \prod_i \Omega_i = \prod_i \frac{(\omega_i + n_i - 1)!}{(\omega_i - 1)!\,n_i!}. \quad (77)$$

The *total* number of configurations Ω for the whole assembly is given by the sum of all possible values of $\tilde{\Omega}$ when we vary n_1, n_2, etc., as we please subject only to the usual restrictive conditions on the whole assembly, assumed isolated, i.e.,

$$\sum_i n_i = N \tag{75a}$$

$$\sum_i n_i \epsilon_i = E. \tag{75b}$$

As we did earlier, we now assume that it will be entirely adequate to seek for a maximum value of $\ln \Omega$, say $\ln \Omega_{\max}$, to determine the equilibrium thermodynamic parameters, and in particular to write for the entropy

$$S = k \ln \Omega_{\max}. \tag{78}$$

If we carry through this program without any further approximation, we arrive directly at the so-called **Bose-Einstein** distribution for an assembly of nonlocalized, independent elements, which we shall consider in more detail later. If on the other hand we impose the *additional* restriction of the so-called Pauli exclusion principle which rigidly limits the occupation number of any individual state to the values 0 or 1, we are led to the so-called **Fermi-Dirac** distribution for an assembly of nonlocalized, independent elements, and this we shall also discuss more fully later.

3.3 THE REAL "CHEMICAL" GAS*

For the present, however, we can proceed immediately by noting that whenever we have to deal with any real "chemical" gas, the densities of atoms or molecules are so low that we may always assume that the occupation numbers (n_i) are very small compared with the available number of elementary states (ω_i); i.e., we may assume quite generally for *any* real gas that $n_i \ll \omega_i$. In that case Eq. 76 reduces to

$$\Omega_i \approx \frac{\omega_i^{n_i}}{n_i!} \tag{76a}$$

* We follow Zemansky (1943) in defining a "chemical" system as one whose macroscopic thermodynamic behavior is adequately described by pressure, volume and temperature (and the concentration of different components if it is not a one-component substance). We shall restrict ourselves here to one-component gases for simplicity.

Thus hydrogen, oxygen, water vapor, carbon dioxide and air under normal conditions are all examples of chemical gases. However the so-called conduction electron gas in a metal is *not* a chemical gas since we have certainly no warrant for ignoring in general the electric charge of the constituent particles.

and thus, corresponding to Eq. 77, we have

$$\tilde{\Omega} \approx \prod_i \frac{\omega_i^{n_i}}{n_i!}. \tag{77a}$$

Our task is once more to seek for a maximum of $\tilde{\Omega}$ subject to the usual restrictive conditions governing N and E. Now in Appendix II (Comment 3) we see for the model of localized elements with energy levels ϵ_i, having degeneracies g_i, that we need to maximize there

$$\tilde{\Omega} = N! \prod_i \frac{g_i^{n_i}}{n_i!}; \tag{79}$$

cf. specifically Eq. 179a of Appendix II, (Comment 3). Thus comparing Eqs. 77a and 79, we see that the maximization of $\tilde{\Omega}$ is formally quite identical in the two problems, since in Eq. 79 the factor $N!$ is merely a constant. Therefore the expression for the "internal distribution," i.e., the "most probable" value of n_i in the gaseous model, may be written down immediately from that derived for the localized model. Thus we have directly

$$\frac{n_i}{N} = \frac{\omega_i \exp(-\epsilon_i/kT)}{\sum_i \omega_i \exp(-\epsilon_i/kT)}, \qquad \text{(cf. Eq. 24}a\text{)}, \tag{80}$$

or

$$\frac{n_i}{\omega_i} = \frac{N \exp(-\epsilon_i/kT)}{\sum_i \omega_i \exp(-\epsilon_i/kT)}. \tag{80a}$$

It follows naturally that if, as we have done previously, we now denote the degeneracy of a *single* energy level by g_i and its occupancy by n_i, we can write

$$\frac{n_i}{g_i} = \frac{N \exp(-\epsilon_i/kT)}{\sum_i g_i \exp(-\epsilon_i/kT)}, \tag{80b*}$$

* If the reader should now wonder why we did not start initially by considering single energy levels, let him recall that it was necessary to group together for our method of analysis sufficiently many (ω_i) neighboring levels so that we could use elementary statistical methods for dealing with the problem. However, once having arrived at Eq. 80a for the relative occupancy (n_i/ω_i) of this group of very closely spaced levels of essentially identical energy, we can *then* proceed directly to Eq. 80b for the probable occupancy of a single energy level.

and the condition for the validity of Eq. 80*b* in the gaseous model is simply that $n_i/g_i \ll 1$. In turn the internal energy E for the "gas-like" model is also given directly by

$$E = N \frac{\sum_i \epsilon_i g_i \exp(-\epsilon_i/kT)}{\sum_i g_i \exp(-\epsilon_i/kT)}, \qquad \text{(cf. Eq. 25).} \qquad (81)$$

Equations 80*b* and 81 then lead us naturally to define once again a partition function per particle for the gaslike model

$$Z = \sum_i g_i e^{-\epsilon_i/kT}, \qquad (82)$$

(as in the "localized" model, cf. Eq. 20*b*, Chapter 1), and all formulas involving the internal energy E, or its derivatives such as the specific heat, remain formally unchanged so that we have again

$$E = \frac{RT^2}{Z}\left(\frac{\partial Z}{\partial T}\right), \qquad \text{(cf. Eq. 21}b\text{),} \qquad (83)$$

as an alternative to Eq. 81, and

$$C_V = R\left[\frac{2T}{Z}\left(\frac{\partial Z}{\partial T}\right) - \frac{T^2}{Z^2}\left(\frac{\partial Z}{\partial T}\right)^2 + \frac{T^2}{Z}\left(\frac{\partial^2 Z}{\partial T^2}\right)\right], \qquad (84)$$

(cf. Eq. 22*d*).

On the other hand, we must notice that the absence of a factor $N!$ in Eq. 77*a* *will* modify explicitly the expressions for the entropy S and for the Helmholtz free energy F. In the gaslike model we have now for the Helmholtz free energy

$$F = -NkT \ln Z + kT \ln N!, \qquad (85)^*$$

* The term involving $N!$ in F or S for the gaslike model as compared with the strictly localizable model has been discussed very frequently by many workers, including Planck himself. (Perhaps Rushbrooke's (1949) discussion in the opening part of his Chapter 3 may be taken as quite typical.) We suggest that it is wiser, at least from an elementary standpoint, to treat the localizable and nonlocalizable models separately as two limiting situations (as we have done) rather than to try to "justify" one model by some transition process from the other. We should in any case notice that the formal agreement in the final results, when we allow for the appropriate factor $N!$ in Ω, is only strictly correct for $n_i \ll \omega_i$, and we ignore any possible restrictions on occupancy of levels. Otherwise, as we have indicated, we are actually led to Bose-Einstein or Fermi-Dirac statistics which no longer correspond even formally to the localizable model.

or in other words for the molar free energy

$$F = -RT(\ln Z - \ln \mathfrak{N} + 1), \quad \text{(contrast with Eq. 20)}, \quad (85a)$$

where $\mathfrak{N}$ as usual is Avogadro's number.

Correspondingly the molar entropy S is given by

$$S = R\left[\ln Z + \frac{T}{Z}\left(\frac{\partial Z}{\partial T}\right) - \ln \mathfrak{N} + 1\right], \quad \text{(contrast with Eq. 22b)}. \quad (86)$$

3.3.1 Partition Function for "Ideal Gases"

Schrödinger's equation for the wave function $\psi(x, y, z)$ of a particle of mass m moving in a region with potential energy $\Phi(x, y, z)$ in a stationary state with energy ϵ reads

$$\frac{\partial^2\psi}{\partial x^2} + \frac{\partial^2\psi}{\partial y^2} + \frac{\partial^2\psi}{\partial z^2} + \frac{2m}{\hbar^2}(\epsilon - \Phi)\psi = 0. \quad (87)$$

If we restrict ourselves (as we shall) to considering problems where each particle is assumed entirely free to move *inside* a container with impermeable walls (e.g., a gas atom in an otherwise empty physical container or a conduction electron in a very idealized metal), we may treat Φ as a constant (conveniently we set $\Phi = 0$), and seek permissible solutions of

$$\frac{\partial^2\psi}{\partial x^2} + \frac{\partial^2\psi}{\partial y^2} + \frac{\partial^2\psi}{\partial z^2} = -\frac{2m\epsilon}{\hbar^2}\psi, \quad (87a)$$

subject to appropriate boundary conditions at the "walls" of the container. This problem is obviously very similar to the task of enumerating the permissible physical vibrations of a crystalline solid which we discussed in Chapter 2 (cf. particularly Eq. 50). For convenience we shall assume again as our boundary condition the "Born cyclic condition," and assume that our container is a cube of side L, and then our permitted solutions for ψ can be written:

$$\psi = Ae^{i\mathbf{k}\cdot\mathbf{r}} \quad \text{(cf. also Eq. 52b)}, \quad (88)$$

where, as before, $\mathbf{k}$ is the wave vector: $[2\pi\mathfrak{n}_1/L, 2\pi\mathfrak{n}_2/L, 2\pi\mathfrak{n}_3/L]$. Substituting Eq. 88 in Eq. 87a, we see that

$$-\frac{4\pi^2}{L^2}(\mathfrak{n}_1^2 + \mathfrak{n}_2^2 + \mathfrak{n}_3^2) = -\frac{2m\epsilon}{\hbar^2},$$

i.e.,

$$\epsilon = \frac{h^2}{2mL^2}(\mathfrak{n}_1^2 + \mathfrak{n}_2^2 + \mathfrak{n}_3^2), \tag{89a}$$

whereas to satisfy the Born cyclic condition demands (as before) that $\mathfrak{n}_1$, $\mathfrak{n}_2$, $\mathfrak{n}_3$ must each individually be an integer

$$\mathfrak{n}_1 \text{ (and } \mathfrak{n}_2\text{, and } \mathfrak{n}_3) = \cdots -2, -1, 0, +1, +2, \ldots, \quad \text{(cf. Eq. 54)}. \tag{89b}$$

Equations 89*a* and 89*b* together determine the permitted energy states for a particle in our idealized "gaslike" model, and to each choice of a triad of (integral) numbers $\mathfrak{n}_1$, $\mathfrak{n}_2$, $\mathfrak{n}_3$ corresponds then a single permissible particle energy state $\epsilon_{\mathfrak{n}_1,\mathfrak{n}_2,\mathfrak{n}_3}$.

The normal vibrations in a solid were seen to be very closely spaced in wave number, and similarly here the particle states are very closely spaced in energy. We may therefore with entirely negligible error replace the summation involved in the partition function Z by an integral. Thus:

$$Z = \sum_{\mathfrak{n}_1,\mathfrak{n}_2,\mathfrak{n}_3} e^{-\epsilon_{\mathfrak{n}_1,\mathfrak{n}_2,\mathfrak{n}_3}/kT} \tag{90a}$$

$$= \iiint_{-\infty}^{+\infty} e^{-h^2(\mathfrak{n}_1^2+\mathfrak{n}_2^2+\mathfrak{n}_3^2)/2mL^2kT}\, d\mathfrak{n}_1\, d\mathfrak{n}_2\, d\mathfrak{n}_3 \tag{90b}$$

$$= \frac{L^3}{h^3}(2\pi mkT)^{3/2} \qquad \left(\text{since} \int_{-\infty}^{+\infty} e^{-t^2}\, dt = \sqrt{\pi}\right);$$

or more generally, if V is the volume of the container,

$$\boxed{Z = V\frac{(2\pi mkT)^{3/2}}{h^3}}. \tag{90c}$$

This is a well-known and rather fundamental classical result for the partition function per particle of an idealized assembly of *independent, nonlocalized* elements. Using now Eq. 86, we have immediately for the entropy per mole of an ideal gas

$$S = R\left(\frac{3}{2}\ln\frac{2\pi mkT}{h^2} - \ln\frac{\mathfrak{N}}{\mathfrak{V}} + \frac{5}{2}\right), \tag{91}$$

where $\mathfrak{V}$ is the molar volume at temperature T and $\mathfrak{N}$ as usual is Avogadro's number. Equation 91 is a quite famous equation, known as the Sackur-Tetrode equation, for the entropy of an ideal gas. From

Eq. 83 we have immediately for the molar internal energy

$$E = \tfrac{3}{2}RT, \tag{92a}$$

and for the molar specific heat at constant volume

$$C_V = \tfrac{3}{2}R. \tag{92b}$$

Since we know explicitly the dependence of the partition function Z on volume V (Eq. 90c), we can also derive immediately the pressure p or in other words the equation of state

$$p = -\left(\frac{\partial F}{\partial V}\right)_{T,N} = NkT\left(\frac{\partial \ln Z}{\partial V}\right)_T, \quad \text{(using Eq. 85)}, \tag{93a}$$

i.e.,

$$p = \frac{RT}{\mathcal{V}}, \tag{93b}$$

if as usual $\mathcal{V}$ is the molar volume at temperature T. Equation 93b is of course the very familiar equation of state for an ideal gas.

3.4 BOSE-EINSTEIN STATISTICS

We now consider the behavior of a gaslike assembly of indistinguishable particles when we do *not* assume $n_i/g_i \ll 1$. If we return to Eq. 77 for $\tilde{\Omega}$ in a gaslike assembly and then seek as usual for Ω_{max} subject to the familiar restrictive conditions:

$$\sum_i n_i = N, \tag{75a}$$

$$\sum_i n_i\epsilon_i = E \tag{75b}$$

without, however, making the approximation $n_i/\omega_i \ll 1$, we arrive at (see Appendix III)

$$n_i = \frac{g_i}{e^{(\epsilon_i/kT)-\alpha} - 1}, \tag{94}$$

in contrast with Eq. 80b. Equation 94 is the basic expression for the internal distribution of a so-called **Bose-Einstein** assembly of independent, nonlocalizable (indistinguishable) "particles" or elements. An important feature is that the parameter α appearing explicitly in Eq. 94 cannot now be readily eliminated. Since α is dimensionless we can also write Eq. 94 as

$$\frac{n_i}{g_i} (\equiv f_i, \text{ say}) = \frac{g_i}{e^{(\epsilon_i - \mu)/kT} - 1}, \tag{94a}$$

where μ has evidently the dimensions of an energy (per particle), and we write $f_i \equiv n_i/g_i$ as is frequently convenient. μ is frequently referred to as the chemical potential, and the physical significance of μ (or α) is commented on in Appendix III. For a "real" (one-component) gas such that the macroscopic behavior is completely represented by p, V, and T, it can be shown that μ is precisely the Gibbs free energy per particle, which for a one-component thermodynamic system is indeed equal to the thermodynamic chemical potential for that system. *Quite generally*, however, one sees that the parameter α, and hence μ, determines physically, when two systems of similar substance are "open" to one another at the same temperature, whether there will be any net flow of particles from one system to the other (cf. again Appendix III). In a similar sense the parameter β (i.e., $-1/kT$) determines physically when two "closed" systems are in contact whether there is any net flow of *energy* from one to the other—in other words, the parameter β determines of course the temperature of an assembly. That is to say, if β is the same for two closed assemblies, then when they are brought into thermal contact with one another (i.e., if an energy transfer becomes possible), there will be no net flow of energy (heat) between the assemblies. Correspondingly with two similar open systems at the same temperature there will be no net mass flow if μ is the same for the two assemblies.

If we are dealing with a real (one-component) gas, μ will be a function of temperature and pressure. In particular, if two containers of similar gas are open to one another at the same temperature, equality of μ for the two containers to ensure no net flow from one container to the other simply implies that the pressures are the same in the two containers—a quite familiar conclusion.* On the other hand, if we try, as physicists do, to apply statistical mechanics to other types of "gaslike" assemblies such as electrons in a metal, then it is perhaps dangerous, and rather unnecessary, to try to identify μ (e.g., in Eq. 94a) specifically as a Gibbs free energy involving pressure p. In fact it is difficult to define in any satisfactorily unique terms what one would really mean by the pressure of conduction electrons in a con-

* These remarks might perhaps suggest that the chemical potential is rather trivial. However, the chemical potentials play a very important role when we are dealing with *multi*component systems, and are then particularly important to the chemist.

ductor. To repeat, what is quite *generally* true, however, is that μ (whatever we choose to call it!) is always the parameter that determines whether between two similar "gaslike" assemblies, open to one another at the same temperature, there will be any net flow of particles from one to the other. That is, for two such systems, say (1) and (2), to be in over-all equilibrium with one another at the same temperature we must have $\mu_1 = \mu_2$, and in principle μ can be evaluated for a given assembly as a function of temperature and density.

The difficulty for a physicist in appreciating the role of μ, in contrast to that of β, is that he already feels at home with the absolute temperature T, and hence he has no difficulty in appreciating the significance of the parameter β $(= -1/kT)$ when he meets this in statistical mechanics for the first time; whereas he is often far from familiar with the "chemical potential" at this stage. If one is dealing only with assemblies of localizable elements or particles (or, one may say, "distinguishable" elements), then in fact the parameter α (or μ) is quite readily eliminated from the final expressions, and the physicist may thus tend to forget that *in general* the factor e^{α} (or $e^{\mu/kT}$) is very important and almost as basic in statistical mechanics as the so-called "Boltzmann factor," $e^{-\epsilon_i/kT}$. In other words, one is often tempted to think that the statistical distribution is effectively determined by the Boltzmann factor alone (although this only becomes true for what we may call classical statistics), and to regard any "departures" from this due to the explicit presence of the factor $e^{\mu/kT}$ (which has every right to be there!) as somehow anomalous. As we shall see, the influence of the factor $e^{\mu/kT}$ can be particularly striking in the behavior of a Bose-Einstein assembly.

3.4.1 Summary of Analytical Situation

Just as the temperature T can be regarded for a given assembly as a function of N, V, and E, so also is α (or μ) another such function. However, as physicists or chemists we usually prefer to work instead with N, V, and T as thermodynamic variables, so that β $(= -1/kT)$ becomes one of our basic parameters, whereas α is now considered as a function of N, V, and T. What we have just said means that at any given temperature and volume we must determine α (or μ) in Eq. 94 or 94*a* as a function of these variables, essentially from the condition that $\sum_i n_i = N$, i.e., for a Bose-Einstein assembly that

$$\sum_i \frac{g_i}{e^{(\epsilon_i - \mu)/kT} - 1} = N. \tag{95}$$

This equation can in principle be solved for μ, and then we can determine the further various thermodynamic properties as functions of N, V, and T. However, from Eq. 95 it is clear that the value of the parameter μ for a particular assembly at a given temperature will depend specifically on the energy levels ϵ_i and the degeneracies g_i of the assembly; in other words, it will depend on the details of the model that we are considering. Thus, as a general rule, we are forced to calculate μ numerically, although in certain limiting cases (broadly speaking, at sufficiently low or high temperatures) we can deal with μ explicitly.

3.4.2 The Classical Limit

If we know a priori that at any particular temperature the density of particles in our "gas" is sufficiently low so that we may assume $n_i \ll g_i$, i.e., $e^{(\epsilon_i-\mu)/kT} - 1 \gg 1$ for *all* values of ϵ_i, then this means that obviously $e^{(\epsilon_i-\mu)/kT} \gg 1$; hence we can now say much more simply from Eq. 94*a*

$$n_i \approx \frac{g_i}{e^{(\epsilon_i-\mu)/kT}}, = g_i e^{\mu/kT} e^{-\epsilon_i/kT}. \tag{96}$$

This means that we can then eliminate under these conditions the explicit appearance of μ by writing

$$\frac{n_i}{N} = \frac{g_i e^{-\epsilon_i/kT}}{\sum_i g_i e^{-\epsilon_i/kT}} \tag{96a}$$

This is exactly the expression that we deduced for the distribution function in a "real" gas (Eq. 80*b*) from the assumption earlier in the proceedings that the density of particles was always sufficiently low, which led in the gaslike model to what are usually called "classical statistics." From Eq. 96 it is clear that the required condition $n_i/g_i \ll 1$ will always be satisfied if the first exponential factor is very much less than unity, or in other words if $\mu/kT \rightarrow -\infty$. For a gas-like model this is a convenient general condition to bear in mind for the validity of classical, or "Maxwellian," statistics. This condition for the transition to classical statistics applies to the particular cases of both Bose-Einstein and Fermi-Dirac assemblies; we shall see this again when we discuss the behavior of liquid helium at very low temperatures (on the Bose-Einstein model) and of the conduction electrons in solids (on the Fermi-Dirac model).

3.5 PAULI EXCLUSION PRINCIPLE AND SPIN

We have seen that Bose-Einstein statistics, strictly speaking, govern the behavior of an assembly of free, indistinguishable particles when there is no a priori restriction on the occupation numbers (n_i). Today we believe that quantum mechanics or wave mechanics offers the most fundamental description we have of the behavior of matter, and in general a solution of Schrödinger's wave equation should provide us with a wave function Ψ from which we can derive the observable properties of the system under examination. If we are considering an assembly of identical (or indistinguishable) "particles," then this wave function will in general involve the coordinates (including particularly some "coordinate(s)" to describe the spin of each particle). Let us consider specifically two of these identical particles, occupying elementary states which we refer to simply as a and b, and we therefore denote the over-all wave function of the assembly for convenience by Ψ_{ab}. Now the wave function *itself* is not regarded as an observable physical quantity, but the product $\Psi^* \cdot \Psi$ (which determines essentially the probability density of particles in terms of the state coordinates) is an observable quantity. The requirement that $\Psi^* \cdot \Psi$ be an observable quantity imposes certain restrictions on the wave function Ψ, and more particularly that Ψ must be either perfectly symmetric or perfectly antisymmetric if we consider interchanging the state coordinates of any two particles.*

Thus if the over-all wave function is *antisymmetric*, this means simply that if any two identical particles in states a and b are supposed to have their state coordinates interchanged, the wave function, say Ψ_{ab}, simply changes sign; i.e., with this simple notation

$$\Psi_{ba} = -\Psi_{ab}. \tag{97a}$$

(We should note, however, that it remains true that $\Psi^*_{ba}\Psi_{ba} = \Psi^*_{ab}\Psi_{ab}$; i.e., the *observable* situation is unchanged as indeed it ought to be.) Now consider the particular case where the state coordinates a and b are identical so that the two particles concerned occupy the *same* state. This then means

$$\Psi_{aa} = -\Psi_{aa}. \tag{97b}$$

Obviously, however, this demands $\Psi_{aa} = 0$, or in other words the situation where two particles occupy the same state is simply not permitted to exist if the wave function is *antisymmetric*. This state

* All of this verbal description is rather crude and will probably not satisfy a professional theorist, but it is hoped that it is sufficient for our purposes.

of affairs is expressed physically by the Pauli Exclusion Principle* that no two particles in an assembly subject to the Pauli Principle may occupy identical elementary quantum states.† In other words, for energy states (ϵ_i) which are singly degenerate ($g_i = 1$), the Exclusion Principle will limit us to $n_i = 0$ or 1, and no other value is permissible for n_i. More generally, under the Exclusion Principle, n_i must lie between zero and g_i as an upper limit, or in other words f_i ($\equiv n_i/g_i$) must satisfy $0 \leq f_i \leq 1$.

On the other hand, if the wave function is *symmetric*, then in the same notation if we interchange the state coordinates of two identical particles in the assembly

$$\Psi_{ab} = \Psi_{ba}, \tag{98a}$$

and hence for two particles with identical state coordinates we have merely now the identity

$$\Psi_{aa} = \Psi_{aa}; \tag{98b}$$

and there is therefore no implied restriction on the occupation of a given particle state by two (or more) particles. That is to say, if the wave function is symmetric, there is *no* restriction from the symmetry conditions on the permissible values of the occupation numbers n_i.

We have already seen that for an assembly of indistinguishable particles with no restriction on n_i, we arrive at **Bose-Einstein** statistics. If on the other hand we impose the Pauli Exclusion Principle on an assembly of indistinguishable particles, we are then led to the so-called **Fermi-Dirac** statistics. It appears to be a basic foundation stone of quantum mechanics that particles with "integral" spin (i.e., spin $= 0, \hbar, 2\hbar, \ldots$) have wave functions which are symmetric; assemblies of such particles (or quasi-particles) may therefore be expected to follow Bose-Einstein statistics; the particles themselves are today often referred to as "bosons." The only familiar cases we shall consider are photons treated as independent "quasi-particles," and He^4 atoms forming liquid helium discussed, following London's (1938) bold lead, as an assembly of independent bosons.

On the other hand, assemblies of particles with "half-integral" spin (spin $= \hbar/2, 3\hbar/2, 5\hbar/2, \ldots$) have wave functions which are antisymmetric; we therefore assume that assemblies of such similar particles will follow Fermi-Dirac statistics. The particles are often known as "fermions." Electrons, protons, and neutrons are all "fermions."

* More briefly in German: *Pauliverbot.*

† First proposed by Pauli around 1925 to account for spectroscopic data, the Pauli Exclusion Principle can be called (and rightly so!) the foundation of the Periodic Table. The extension of the idea from electrons in a more or less isolated atom to more general assemblies (and particularly to the conduction electrons in a metal) came a few years later (Sommerfeld; Fermi, Dirac).

We shall consider the conduction electrons in a metal, and also mention liquid He^3 (again as a brash first approximation) as examples of Fermi-Dirac assemblies.

3.6 FERMI-DIRAC STATISTICS

To embody the very stringent restriction of the Pauli Principle ($n_i = 0$ or 1 *only*, for a nondegenerate level) to arrive at Fermi-Dirac statistics, it is convenient to do our "counting" afresh for calculating Ω (see Appendix IV). We also show in Appendix V how a rather more general (and perhaps illuminating) common approach can be made which includes both Bose-Einstein and Fermi-Dirac situations.

With our usual assumption for a "gaslike" model that the energy levels are extremely closely spaced in energy, we find (see Appendix IV) that the most probable distribution is given by

$$n_i = \frac{g_i}{e^{(\epsilon_i/kT-\alpha)} + 1}, \tag{99}$$

or

$$n_i = \frac{g_i}{e^{(\epsilon_i-\mu)/kT} + 1}, \tag{99a}$$

where again the parameter α (or μ) is determined by the condition that the total number of particles in the assembly is held fixed, i.e., $\sum_i n_i = N$, and μ as usual is referred to as the "chemical potential." In a Fermi-Dirac assembly, as we shall see in a moment, the chemical potential is rather easy to identify physically at low temperatures; the chemical potential is also frequently denoted by ζ in Fermi-Dirac statistics, so that we write more usually

$$f_i \equiv \frac{n_i}{g_i} = \frac{1}{e^{(\epsilon_i-\zeta)/kT} + 1}. \tag{99b}$$

3.6.1 General Behavior of a Fermi-dirac Assembly

Let us consider first the situation at very low temperatures. If we recall our earlier discussions, and particularly the behavior of crystalline solids, we naturally expect that at low temperatures the whole assembly will tend to sink into the state of lowest possible total energy. In an idealized Bose-Einstein assembly of particles we know of nothing to prevent all the particles from occupying the lowest particle energy state ($\epsilon = 0$) at absolute zero; in fact the enormous concentration of particles which can result ultimately in this lowest energy level produces some rather remarkable behavior in a Bose-Einstein assembly at sufficiently low temperatures. However, the restriction of the Pauli Exclusion Principle on "fermions" will, as we have seen, only permit *one* particle per elementary state; therefore the best that can be done, so to speak, at very low temperatures (more particularly $T = 0$) is to "pack in" the particles into the lowest *permissible* energy states at the rate of one per elementary state. Thus at $T = 0$ we would expect to find f_i $(\equiv n_i/g_i) = 1$ quite uniformly up to some particular particle energy, say $\tilde{\epsilon}$; at which point we have now "packed in" all the N particles of the assembly, and consequently thereafter $n_i = 0$ (i.e., $f_i = 0$) for all *higher* energy levels. Perhaps we should note immediately what has happened physically: the whole assembly at $T = 0$ will now be in a state of minimum total energy E, *subject to the requirements of the Pauli Principle.* At the same time, because the distribution function (f_i) is in the limit either precisely unity or precisely zero, this means that in this limit $(T = 0)$ there is only one distinguishable configuration (complexion) of the whole assembly; i.e., we have in the limit $\Omega = 1$, and hence S $(= k \ln \Omega) = 0$. We are glad to see that once again the general requirements of the Third Law of Thermodynamics will be satisfied.

This particle energy $\tilde{\epsilon}$ required for us to "pack in" the particles at absolute zero can be quite large for light particles such as electrons. Thus even at $T = 0$ the whole assembly can have a very considerable total energy (the zero-point energy of the whole system), but let us repeat that the system "arranges itself" at $T = 0$ so as to have the *minimum possible* total energy, and at the same time there is no "disorder" left in the sense that $S \rightarrow 0$. We have seen that the limiting occupied particle energy state $(\tilde{\epsilon})$ is determined by the number of particles N to be "packed in," and we know already that the chemical potential ζ is also determined in this way. So it is not surprising that the chemical potential (per particle) at absolute zero (say ζ_0) is just such that ζ_0 is precisely equal to $\tilde{\epsilon}$ in Fermi-Dirac statistics. That is to say, f_i has the simple form at $T = 0$ shown in Fig. 12, which may readily be checked by considering the behavior of Eq. 99*b* for $T \rightarrow 0$. Thus in Eq. 99*b* for $T \rightarrow 0$ and $\epsilon_i < \zeta_0$, the exponential term vanishes in the denominator so that $f_i = 1$, whereas for $\epsilon_i > \zeta_0$ the exponential term tends to infinity so that $f_i = 0$. Let us now estimate roughly ζ_0. From Eq. 89*a* we have for the permitted energy levels ϵ of free particles in a cubic container of side L

$$\epsilon = \frac{h^2 \mathrm{n}^2}{2mL^2}, \qquad (89a)$$

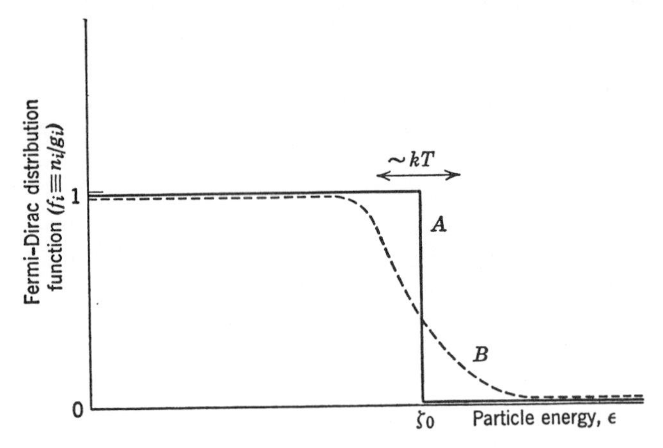

FIG. 12. **Rough sketch** of variation of Fermi-Dirac distribution function $f(\epsilon)$ as a function of particle energy ϵ.

(Full line) A. Behavior at absolute zero ($T = 0$). All particle states are occupied up to $\epsilon = \zeta_0$ (i.e., $f(\epsilon) = 1$ for $\epsilon < \zeta_0$), and are unoccupied for $\epsilon > \zeta_0$ (i.e., $f(\epsilon) = 0$ for $\epsilon > \zeta_0$).

(Broken line) B. Behavior for some temperature, T, such that $kT \ll \zeta_0$ (i.e., $T \ll T_0$, where T_0 is the "Fermi degeneracy temperature" of the assembly such that $kT_0 \equiv \zeta_0$).

where

$$\mathfrak{n}^2 = \mathfrak{n}_1^2 + \mathfrak{n}_2^2 + \mathfrak{n}_3^2.$$

It is easy to see that if each energy level is permitted to be occupied by only one particle,* the maximum value of $\mathfrak{n}$ (say $\tilde{\mathfrak{n}}$) is such that

* More strictly the energy levels of Eq. 89*a* are the *translational* energy levels for the particles, and we have still to include a "spin coordinate" for the fermions. If we are dealing with the conduction electrons in a metal (i.e., "fermions" of spin $\hbar/2$, often referred to as "spin 1/2"), then it is usual to assume that with each of these translational energy states *two* separate spin states may be associated. This means finally that the total number of occupied states at $T = 0$ under the restriction of the Pauli Principle is given by:

$$2 \iiint d\mathfrak{n}_1\, d\mathfrak{n}_2\, d\mathfrak{n}_3 = N, \qquad \text{i.e., } 8\pi \int_0^{\tilde{\mathfrak{n}}} \mathfrak{n}^2\, d\mathfrak{n} = N, \tag{100a}$$

where $\tilde{\mathfrak{n}}$ is the maximum value required of $\mathfrak{n}$, and the factor of 2 in the first equation refers to the 2 spin states with each translational state. Thus finally

$$\tilde{\mathfrak{n}}^3 = \frac{3N}{8\pi}. \tag{100b}$$

Equation 101 should then read more precisely:

$$\zeta_0 = \frac{h^2}{8m}\left(\frac{3}{\pi} N_1\right)^{2/3}. \tag{101a}$$

$\bar{n}^3 \approx N$, i.e., $\bar{n}^2 \approx N^{2/3}$. Hence

$$\zeta_0 \approx \frac{h^2 N^{2/3}}{mL^2}, = \frac{h^2}{m} N_1^{2/3}, \qquad (101)^*$$

where N_1 is the number of particles per unit volume. Thus ζ_0 involves the density of particles (N_1) and is *inversely* proportional to the particle mass m.

Consider first any real gas at normal pressures presumed to obey Fermi-Dirac statistics. Typical atomic weights are such that $m \sim 10^{-22}$ grams, and we might certainly assume that the gas density would never exceed perhaps 10^{20}/cc. Then $\zeta_0 \sim 10^{-17}$ erg, which is a rather small energy per particle; if we wish to express ζ_0 as an equivalent (classical) thermal energy by writing $kT_0 = \zeta_0$, then T_0 is of order 0.1°K. The only real gas that could exist at all at this sort of temperature is the vapor of liquid or solid helium, and moreover the density (N_1) would then be *extremely* low. Thus for real gases we can neglect entirely the zero-point energy of the assembly. This provides a further confirmation that, when we are dealing with any real gas, classical statistics are quite adequate for the purpose, and we can ignore any refinements of Fermi-Dirac or Bose-Einstein statistics.

Consider, however, Eq. 101 in the light of *liquid* helium. Then $m \sim 10^{-23}$ gram and $N_1 \sim 10^{22}$/cc. Thus $\zeta_0 \sim 10^{-15}$ erg and T_0 is in the order of, but something less than, 10°K. This is now entirely comparable with the liquefaction temperature of helium (~4°K for He^4 and ~3°K for He^3, both under one atmosphere pressure). Broadly speaking, this then means that we must be prepared to find that symmetry conditions (i.e., the use of Fermi-Dirac or Bose-Einstein statistics, whichever is appropriate) are indeed of importance in the analysis of the behavior of liquid helium.

Now what of the problem of conduction electrons in a metal or semiconductor, or of the thermionic electrons in a vacuum tube? If

* An alternative rather crude way of regarding this result is this: If a typical particle has momentum p, then $\Delta p \cdot \Delta r \approx h$, where r is a positional coordinate for a particle. With N_1 particles per unit volume we might say that the "volume available per particle," Δv is such that $\Delta v \sim N_1^{-1}$, or in other words $\Delta r \sim N_1^{-1/3}$ (and crudely localizing each particle to a separate element of volume, Δv, in this way will satisfy the Pauli Exclusion Principle). Hence $\Delta p \sim h/\Delta r \sim hN_1^{1/3}$, and thus finally the typical energy per particle arising from the Uncertainty Principle applied in this way would be $\epsilon \sim (\Delta p)^2/m \sim h^2 N_1^{2/3}/m$ (cf. Eq. 101).

we assume that in an average metal we have about one conduction electron per atom, then typically $N_1 \sim 10^{22}$/cc, the electron mass $\sim 10^{-27}$ gram, and thus $\zeta_0 \sim 10^{-11}$ erg. This is now a rather large particle energy of the order of 10 ev; if we write again $T_0 = \zeta_0/k$, then T_0 is of the order 10^{5}°K. If on the other hand we were dealing with electrons in a vacuum tube, which we might think of as being closer to a real gas, we might perhaps meet an electron density $N_1 \sim 10^{11}$/cc, and in this case very roughly $\zeta_0 \sim 10^{-18}$ erg. This is once more a very small particle energy of around 10^{-6} ev, or equivalently $T_0 \sim 10^{-2}$°K. What all this means is that for electrons in a vacuum tube, the electron density is so low that the electrons can be treated by classical statistics quite adequately at *all* temperatures where such a "gas" of electrons has any physical importance. On the other hand, if we choose to treat (as we frequently do) the conduction electrons in a *metal* as a gaslike statistical assembly (obeying Fermi-Dirac statistics), then the properties are *very different* from those that we would expect of a classical gas.* The very high zero-point energy of the condution electrons typified by ζ_0 ($= kT_0$), means that the behavior at any temperature T of this Fermi-Dirac assembly will only differ slightly from its properties at absolute zero unless and until T begins to be comparable with T_0. In metals we have seen that $T_0 \sim 10^{5}$°K, and any metallic solid will certainly have vaporized long before it reaches a temperature of this magnitude (at least at normal pressure). Consequently we would never be justified in treating the conduction electrons in a metal as a classical system, and indeed their general behavior is quite different from that of a classical gas. With a semiconductor the situation will depend very naturally on what may be the actual density (N_1) of conduction electrons in any particular material. The conduction electron density N_1 in a semiconductor depends in turn generally on the temperature, and it is quite common in semiconductors for the conduction electron density at some temperatures to be sufficiently low that classical ideas may be quite adequate; whereas at other temperatures we must take account specifically of Fermi-Dirac statistics. As the changeover occurs from

* It is particularly to Drude (1900) that we owe the model of conduction electrons in a metal as a more or less freely moving "gas." In his day it would certainly have been difficult to see logically how the electrons could *remain* free to move around at very low temperatures without "condensing" back on to the ionic lattice. In rough terms we can say today that the free electron gas model is essentially justified by the high zero-point energy of the assembly; in other words, the electrons, even at absolute zero, have on the average a very high kinetic energy which is sufficient to "overcome" the electrostatic attraction between the electrons and the ionic lattice.

approximately classical behavior to where we must use the more accurate Fermi-Dirac expressions, it is usual to say that the electron gas is becoming "degenerate." In a typical metal, we may say that at all normal temperatures the conduction electron gas is highly degenerate in this sense.

3.6.2 Behavior of Idealized Fermi-dirac Gas

We have mentioned previously that the particle states (energy levels) in gaslike models are always extremely closely spaced in energy. From a first crude guess, the energy spacing $\Delta\epsilon$ between neighboring levels will be of order $\Delta\epsilon \sim h^2/mV^{2/3}$. Let us consider an extremely unfavorable case where we are dealing with a very small particle of matter of about 1μ in linear dimensions ($V \sim 10^{-12}$ cm^3), and we inquire about the energy level spacings for free electrons ($m \sim 10^{-27}$ gram). Then $\Delta\epsilon \sim 10^{-18}$ erg, which corresponds to an equivalent temperature of only about 10^{-2}°K. In all other cases, where the volume involved would be larger and the mass might well be considerably greater, the energy spacing $\Delta\epsilon$ would even be much smaller than this. In other words, we would expect that we would almost invariably be entirely justified in treating the energy levels in any gaslike model as a continuum* and so be justified in replacing sums over the energy levels by integrations. We already followed this procedure when dealing with the real gas (the transition from Eq. 90*a* to Eq. 90*b*), and the general philosophy is of course very similar to what we did earlier when dealing with the normal vibrations of a solid. The particle energy states in the ideal gaslike model are determined by

$$\epsilon = \frac{h^2(\mathfrak{n}_1{}^2 + \mathfrak{n}_2{}^2 + \mathfrak{n}_3{}^2)}{2mV^{2/3}} \equiv \frac{h^2\mathfrak{n}^2}{2mV^{2/3}}, \qquad \text{(i.e., Eq. 89}a\text{)} \qquad (102)$$

and the *number* of these states in the small interval $d\mathfrak{n}$, say $g(\mathfrak{n})\,d\mathfrak{n}$, is

$$g(\mathfrak{n})\,d\mathfrak{n} = 4\pi\mathfrak{n}^2\,d\mathfrak{n}, \qquad (103)$$

* The only case where this procedure is *not* warranted is when we deal with an idealized Bose-Einstein assembly at sufficiently low temperatures, more specifically below the so-called Bose-Einstein "condensation temperature" (see Section 3.7). The situation then arises that an enormous concentration of particles builds up without restriction in the lowest particle state ($\epsilon = 0$), and the usual approximation to the sum by an integral happens to neglect precisely this one energy state. It is therefore necessary in this isolated special situation to take individual account of the lowest particle state.

when we bear in mind that a single state occupies unit volume in the space defined by the Cartesian coordinates $\mathfrak{n}_1$, $\mathfrak{n}_2$, $\mathfrak{n}_3$ (cf. Eq. 89*b*). It is now convenient to re-express Eq. 103 by using Eq. 102, so that the number of states in an *energy* interval $d\epsilon$ can be written:

$$g(\epsilon)\,d\epsilon = 2\pi\left(\frac{2mV^{2/3}}{h^2}\right)^{3/2}\epsilon^{1/2}\,d\epsilon = \frac{2\pi}{h^3}\,V(2m)^{3/2}\epsilon^{1/2}\,d\epsilon. \tag{104}$$

The number of states per unit volume in the energy interval $d\epsilon$ is known as the "density of states," say $g_1(\epsilon)$. Thus for the idealized gas model in general

$$\boxed{g_1(\epsilon) = \frac{2\pi}{h^3}\,(2m)^{3/2}\epsilon^{1/2}}\,. \tag{104a}$$

In deriving Eq. 104*a* we have not taken any account explicitly of spin. If for example we are dealing with fermions of spin $\frac{1}{2}$ (e.g., the conduction electrons in a metal), and assume as usual that two spin states may be associated with each translational state, we must multiply the right-hand side of Eq. 104 and 104*a* by a factor of 2.

[This expression for $g_1(\epsilon)$ with its specific dependence on $\epsilon^{1/2}$ is naturally that appropriate to an idealized noninteracting gas model with particles of mass m, but it is often assumed when dealing with problems such as electronic conduction in metals that the density of states may have more general forms where in particular

(1) The dependence on particle energy ϵ is no longer necessarily proportional to $\epsilon^{1/2}$, and
(2) An "effective mass" m^* replaces the usual mass m.

This sort of generalization of $g_1(\epsilon)$ from the ideal gas model is intended, to some degree of approximation, to take account of interaction of the particles (more specifically electrons) with one another and/or with the atomic lattice.]

If we turn now specifically to the idealized **Fermi-Dirac** gas, we can write down the entropy S using Eq. 211 in Appendix IV, and replace the summation there by an integration over all values of the particle energy ϵ, i.e.,

$$S = -k\int_0^\infty \{f(\epsilon)\ln f(\epsilon) + [1 - f(\epsilon)]\ln[1 - f(\epsilon)]\}g(\epsilon)\,d\epsilon. \tag{105}$$

Correspondingly we have for the total energy of the assembly

$$E = \int_0^\infty \epsilon f(\epsilon)g(\epsilon)\,d\epsilon, \tag{106}$$

where in Eqs. 105 and 106

$$f(\epsilon) = \frac{1}{e^{(\epsilon - \zeta)/kT} + 1} \quad \text{(cf. Eq. 99}b\text{).} \tag{107}$$

To complete the evaluation of S and E [or of any other thermodynamic parameter expressed in terms of $f(\epsilon)$], we must, as pointed out earlier, evaluate ζ, the "chemical potential" or "Fermi energy," at any given temperature through the restrictive condition: $\sum_i n_i = N$, or in other words, by using the density of states $g(\epsilon)$, we have to satisfy

$$N = \int_0^\infty f(\epsilon)g(\epsilon)\, d\epsilon. \tag{108}$$

Behavior at Low Temperatures. The *general* evaluation of Eqs. 105, 106, and 108 requires detailed numerical calculations (cf., e.g., Wilson, 1953, p. 330, et seq.; McDougall and Stoner, 1938), but we can see the qualitative behavior quite readily. So long as the "thermal energy" kT at any given temperature T is small compared with ζ_0, the chemical potential or Fermi energy at absolute zero, the chemical potential ζ at that temperature T will not change very much from its value (ζ_0) at $T = 0$. Consequently $f(\epsilon)$ remains very close to unity up to ϵ close to ζ_0, and then goes rapidly to zero thereafter (cf. Fig. 12). Only within a small energy range in the order of kT around ζ_0 does $f(\epsilon)$ change rapidly from (practically) unity towards zero. Let us then approximate very simply by assuming: $f(\epsilon) = 1$ up to $\epsilon = \zeta_0 - \alpha kT$; $f(\epsilon) = \frac{1}{2}$ in the next small energy interval to $\zeta_0 + \alpha kT$; and $f(\epsilon) = 0$ for all higher energies, where α is a numerical factor in the order of unity. With this rather crude approximation we find readily for the molar entropy of an ideal free electron gas

$$S \sim R\frac{T}{T_0}, \tag{109a*}$$

where as usual the "Fermi degeneracy temperature" $T_0 \equiv \zeta_0/k$, and for the molar energy we find

$$(E - E_0) \sim RT\frac{T}{T_0}, \tag{110a}$$

* The approximation actually gives: $S = 3\alpha \ln 2 \cdot R(T/T_0)$, so that to agree with Eq. 109*b* below would require: $\alpha = \pi^2/6 \ln 2$.

Perhaps we should remark that the crude approximation used does not yield strictly consistent numerical values for S and E, although the general behavior is quite correct.

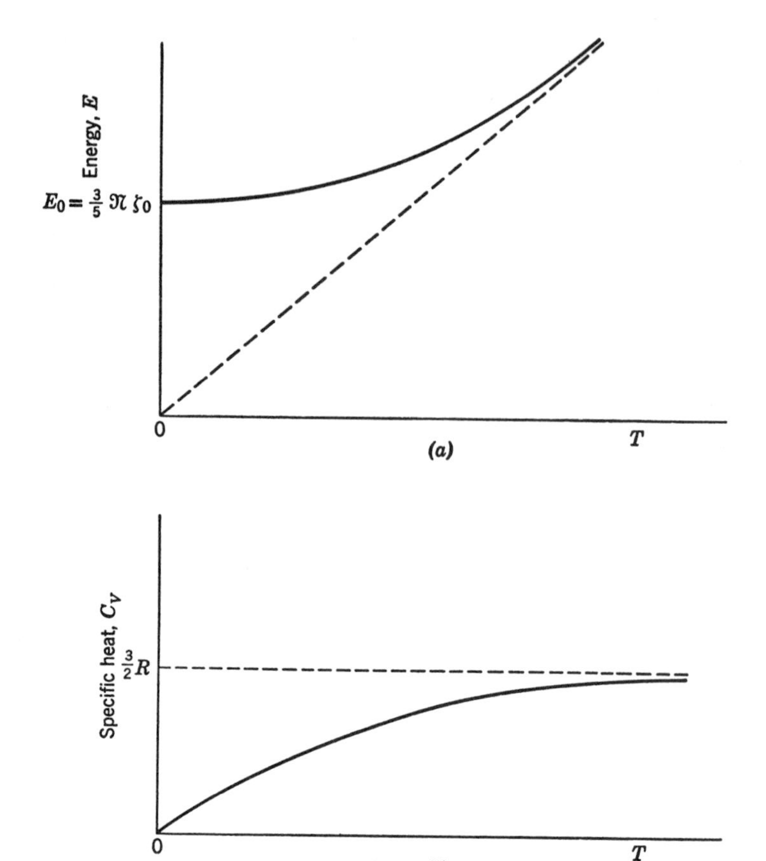

FIG. 13. General thermodynamic behavior of idealized Fermi-Dirac "gas."

(*a*) **Rough sketch** of the dependence of the molar energy E on temperature. At "low" temperatures ($kT \ll \zeta_0$; i.e., $T \ll T_0$), $E \approx E_0 + (\pi^2/4)R(T^2/T_0)$, where E_0, the zero-point energy of the whole assembly, is given by $E_0 = \frac{3}{5}\mathfrak{N}\zeta_0$. At sufficiently "high" temperatures, E approaches smoothly the classical behavior indicated by the dashed line, i.e., $E \approx \frac{3}{2}RT$.

(*b*) **Rough sketch** of the dependence of the molar specific heat C_V on temperature. At "low" temperatures ($T \ll T_0$) the specific heat varies linearly with temperature, i.e., $C_V \approx (\pi^2/2)R(T/T_0)$. At sufficiently "high" temperatures, C_V approaches smoothly the classical limit indicated by the dashed line, i.e., $C_V \approx \frac{3}{2} R$.

where E_0 is the molar (zero-point) energy at $T = 0$ ($E_0 = \frac{3}{5}\mathfrak{N}\zeta_0$). In Eqs. 109$a$ and 110a numerical factors of something greater than unity are omitted. A more exact evaluation (cf., e.g., Wilson, 1953, p. 144 et seq.; Mott and Jones, 1936, p. 178 et seq.) yields

$$S = \frac{\pi^2}{2} R \frac{T}{T_0}, \tag{109b}$$

and

$$(E - E_0) = \frac{\pi^2}{4} RT \frac{T}{T_0}. \tag{110b}$$

From Eqs. 109b or 110b we have immediately for the molar specific heat

$$C_V = T\left(\frac{dS}{dT}\right)_V = \left(\frac{\partial E}{\partial T}\right)_V = \frac{\pi^2}{2} R \frac{T}{T_0}. \tag{111}$$

The linear dependence of the entropy and specific heat with temperature (so long as $T \ll T_0$) is particularly characteristic of a "degenerate" Fermi-Dirac gas.

Behavior at Sufficiently High Temperatures. As the temperature T becomes comparable with the degeneracy temperature T_0, the behavior of a Fermi-Dirac "gas" ultimately becomes essentially classical, so that $E \approx \frac{3}{2}RT$ and $C_V \approx \frac{3}{2}R$. In an idealized Fermi-Dirac gas the transition from "low" to "sufficiently high" temperatures proceeds smoothly, so that the whole behavior is as indicated in Fig. 13.

3.6.3 General Remarks about Conduction Electrons

In crude terms we may interpret physically the low temperature behavior of the energy and specific heat by saying that, as we heat up the assembly, only a fraction $\sim T/T_0$ of the particles around the Fermi energy (ζ_0) are free to change their individual states and so take up a thermal energy of about kT per particle. Thus in particular the molar specific heat C_V for a "degenerate" Fermi-Dirac gas is less than the classical value ($C_V \sim R$) by a factor of the order of T/T_0 (cf. Eq. 111). For conduction electrons in metals, as already mentioned, T_0 is typically as high as 10^4°K to 10^5°K (see Table 6), and thus at room temperature the factor T/T_0 is usually only a few percent. Consequently the contribution to the total specific heat of a metal from the conduction electrons is generally rather small, and as a first approximation it is usually neglected at normal temperatures in comparison with the *lattice* specific heat.

TABLE 6

ESTIMATES OF FERMI DEGENERACY TEMPERATURE T_0 OF THE MONOVALENT METALS. ($T_0 \equiv \zeta_0/k$, AND ζ_0, THE FERMI ENERGY, IS GIVEN BY EQ. 101a; WE ASSUME IDEALLY ONE FREE ELECTRON PER ATOM IN THESE METALS)

	Metal	T_0 (°K)
(Alkali metals)		
	Li	5.5×10^4
	Na	3.65×10^4
	K	2.4×10^4
	Rb	2.1×10^4
	Cs	$\sim 1.75 \times 10^4$
(Group IB metals)		
	Cu	8.2×10^4
	Ag	6.4×10^4
	Au	6.4×10^4

However, we should notice that at *sufficiently* low temperatures (see Chapter 2) the lattice specific heat will ultimately decay as T^3 towards zero, and at that stage the electronic specific heat, decaying linearly with T, must *ultimately* dominate the situation. In typical metals this may be expected to occur at temperatures somewhat below 10°K. The general comparative behavior of the electronic and lattice specific heats in a typical metal is sketched in Fig. 14.

Metals in Contact. When two metals (or for that matter any two electronic conductors), say (1) and (2), are placed in contact, this means physically that the conduction electrons are more or less free to move from one conductor to the other. In chemical language the two electron-assemblies are "open" to one another. We would therefore expect that when equilibrium is achieved, the two metals being at the same temperature, the chemical potentials in the two conductors must equalize. This indeed happens, but the mechanism is more complex than that which would occur for more "straightforward" chemical gases (and hence our earlier warnings about the possible dangers of always trying to identify μ or ζ with familiar expressions for the Gibbs free energy of a real gas).

With two chemical gases open to one another, a net flow of gas would in general take place from one container to the other, altering significantly the concentration and pressure in the two containers until the required equality of chemical potential was reached. On the other hand, electrons in metals or other conductors are of course strongly charged electrostatically, and if any significant net flow takes place from one metal to another, the metal losing the electrons would rapidly become positively charged in relation to the other (and indeed this is the precise origin of the so-called "contact potential" or "Volta potential"). We may say then that when two metals are placed in contact, a relatively tiny number of electrons will flow from one to the

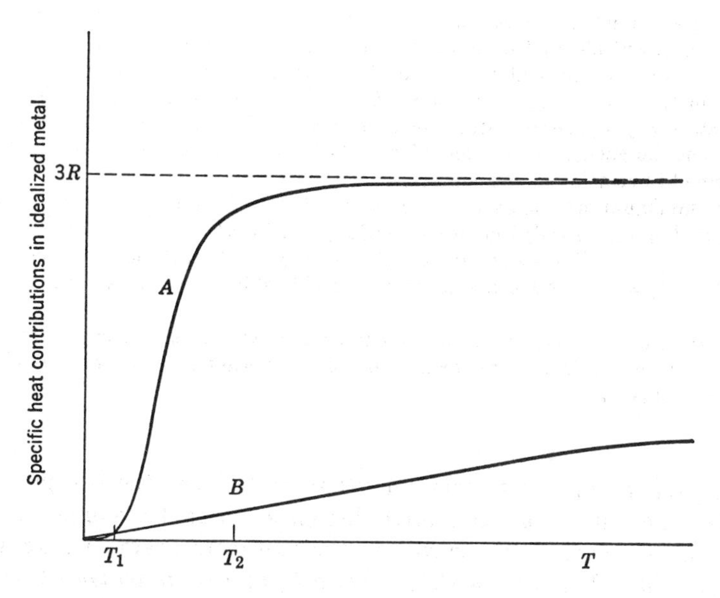

FIG. 14. **Very rough** sketch of qualitative behavior of specific heat contributions in a typical (but idealized) metal.

A. Theoretical behavior of *idealized lattice* molar specific heat (C_{latt}), arising from harmonic thermal vibrations.

B. Theoretical behavior of idealized specific heat due to conduction electrons (C_{el}), arising from translational motion of conduction electrons.

T_2 indicates some "normal" temperature (typically room temperature) where C_{latt} is more or less classical ($C_{\text{latt}} \approx 3R$), whereas C_{el} is still relatively small and varying linearly with T. T_1 indicates a sufficiently low temperature (typically 10°K and below) where C_{latt} is diminishing rapidly toward zero ($C_{\text{latt}} \propto T^3$), and C_{el} (still diminishing *linearly* with T) thus begins to dominate the situation.

In general in a metal the electron degeneracy temperature, T_0, where C_{el} would approach classical behavior ($C_{\text{el}} \rightarrow \frac{3}{2}R$), would be *very* much higher than T_2 (typically $T_0 \sim 10^4$ to 10^5°K).

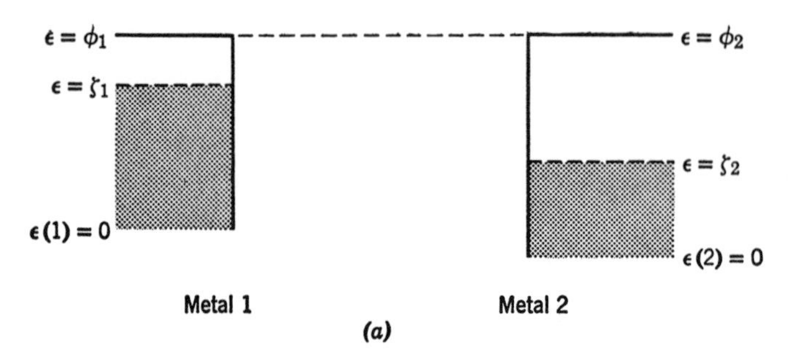

FIG 15*a* and *b*. Sketches to illustrate electron energy levels in idealized metals before and after contact.

(*a*) Two (uncharged) metals before contact. The electron energy levels, $\epsilon = 0$, represent ideally the states of a free electron "at rest" in each metal. The levels ζ_1 and ζ_2 represent the chemical potentials (Fermi energies) of free electrons in the two metals as measured from the states $\epsilon = 0$. The shaded areas indicate occupied electron states in each metal. The levels $\epsilon = \phi_1$ and $\epsilon = \phi_2$ represent the energy of electrons "just outside" each metal, and these levels are presumed to coincide before contact.

The minimum net energy to "extract" an electron from a metal (which can be measured rather directly) defines essentially the "work function" of that metal. This energy, say W, is evidently given by $W = \phi - \zeta$ in each case. Hence metal 2 (thus $W_2 = \phi_2 - \zeta_2$) has evidently a considerably larger work function than metal 1.

(*Note:* The definition given for work function is strictly speaking only valid at $T = 0$ where the division between occupied and vacant electron states is ideally perfectly sharp.)

other, setting up a net potential difference between the two pieces of metals (i.e., the "Volta potential difference"), but the volume concentrations of conduction electrons in the two metals remain essentially unchanged. This means that in turn ζ_1 and ζ_2 *as measured respectively from the free electron state* $\epsilon = 0$ *in* **each** *metal* remain essentially unchanged. In physical terms we can say that the zero-point energy (ideally kinetic energy) of the conduction electrons in each metal remains unchanged when the metals are placed in contact, but the chemical potentials (or "Fermi levels") of the electrons in the two metals are brought into coincidence, if we measure electron energy in *both* cases from an external *common* reference energy level. This common reference level is usually regarded as that of an isolated charge "at infinity" (i.e., a charge far removed from any other charges). The situation is indicated in Fig. 15; perhaps the most vital thing to realize is that the electron states $\epsilon = 0$ in two metals in thermodynamic equilibrium *differ* from one another even when in contact, i.e., precisely by

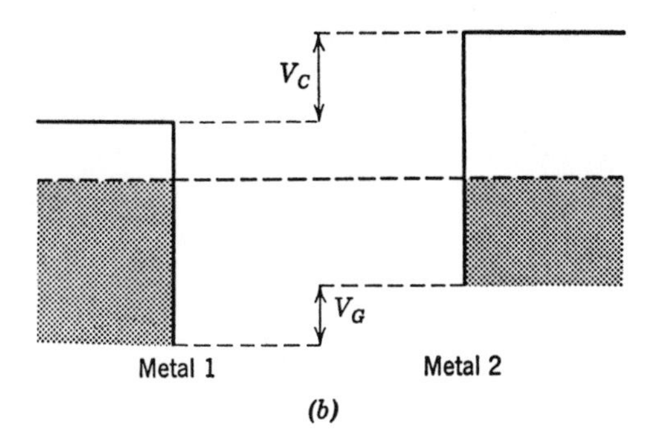

FIG. 15(*b*). Two metals in thermal equilibrium after contact. It is assumed that the various electron energy *differences* are essentially unchanged in *each* metal, but now the levels corresponding to the chemical potentials of the two metals coincide. The net difference between the energies of an electron just outside metal 1 and just outside metal 2 then gives rise to the "contact potential-difference" (Volta potential) V_C which can be measured directly. The energy difference that would exist between the states of free electrons ideally "at rest" in the interior of each metal gives rise to the so-called "Galvani potential-difference," V_G. Obviously the Galvani potential difference is determined by the differences of the two "Fermi" energies (ζ_1, ζ_2) as measured from $\epsilon = 0$ in each metal. Since however, the Galvani potential is only defined in terms of an idealized model (i.e., involving the electron states "at rest" ($\epsilon = 0$) in the two metals), it *cannot* be measured directly. However its *derivative* with temperature (i.e., involving $d\zeta_1/dT$, $d\zeta_2/dT$) appears explicitly, for example, in thermoelectric phenomena.

It should also be obvious that the Volta potential-difference V_C is directly determined by the *difference* of the two "work functions" (W_1, W_2). This is a satisfying conclusion, since the work functions and the Volta potential-difference are all experimentally measurable.

the difference of the Fermi energies ζ_1 and ζ_2 as measured from the electron states $\epsilon = 0$ in the respective metals.

This conclusion can seem a little surprising at first, and particularly so if one visualizes the conduction electrons too literally as a simple particle gas. On this idealized model the conduction electron state $\epsilon = 0$ in each metal corresponds to a conduction electron "at rest" in each metal. One is perhaps then tempted to expect that these states should *always* coincide. We must, however, remember that we are dealing physically with charged negative particles in a highly charged positive environment (the lattice ions), and any slight imbalance of charge can lead to large (electrostatic) energy differences. It is indeed in this way, as already pointed out, that the initial, very small electron transfer from one metal to the other suffices to produce the relatively large Volta (or contact) potential difference. Moreover, it is wise in any case to remember that in any *real* metal, the wave function of a conduction electron in the particle ground-state [$\epsilon = 0$; i.e., having essentially a very small (ideally zero) kinetic energy] is probably very different from the wave function of an idealized "free electron." It is probably *only* for electron states with energies not far from the Fermi level ($\epsilon \approx \zeta$) that the electron states in a metal are in fact well approximated by free electron wave functions.

What remains true in the end is that the very idealized free electron Fermi-Dirac gas model is a remarkably good over-all approximation for many purposes in the theory of metals and of other conducting solids. It is used with considerable confidence not only in the analysis of equilibrium phenomena (such as discussions of specific heats) but also in "transport phenomena" such as electrical conductivity and thermoelectric power.

Fermi-Dirac statistics are also applied to the analysis of liquid He^3, but it is probably best to consider first the problem of liquid He^4; therefore we now discuss that particular question.

3.7 THE LIQUID HELIUM PROBLEM

3.7.1 Liquid Helium as an Assembly of Localized Particles

Two basic features characterize an assembly of helium atoms in general: the atoms are very light (atomic mass 4 or 3),* and the interatomic forces are very weak because we are dealing with "chemically inert" atoms (i.e., atoms with "closed" electronic shells). Consider now Heisenberg's Uncertainty Principle $\Delta p_x \cdot \Delta x \sim h$. If we regard liquid helium as an assembly of more or less *localized* particles of mass m with an average interatomic spacing of a, then we should expect the Uncertainty Principle to demand roughly a zero-point kinetic energy per atom of ($\epsilon = p^2/2m$) about

$$\epsilon \sim \frac{h^2}{ma^2}, \tag{112}$$

and for a given interatomic spacing a this energy is obviously greatest when the atomic mass m is small as it is in helium when compared with other chemical substances. At the same time the interatomic forces, as we have just said, will be very weak between the "inert" helium atoms, and thus on both counts we might expect zero-point energy to play a very important role in the behavior of liquid helium

* He^4 and He^3 are the only two isotopes with which we concern ourselves here.

at low temperatures. Put in its roughest terms* we can guess that helium may have a hard job condensing at all (i.e., for the very weak attractive interatomic forces to overcome the effective repulsive "force" of the zero-point energy), and moreover that He^3 (the lighter isotope) would have an even harder job condensing than He^4.

Broadly speaking these guesses are borne out by the facts that

(1) Liquid helium is very considerably lighter than would be the case if the atoms were more or less "close-packed."

(2) The normal liquefaction temperature of He^3 ($\sim$3°K) is even lower than that of He^4 ($\sim$4°K).

(3) Both liquid helium isotopes actually require the addition of a positive external pressure to produce a crystalline solid at all.

3.7.2 Liquid Helium as a "Gaslike" Assembly

On this general basis it is then perhaps much more reasonable than it would be with any other liquid to attempt to discuss the liquid helium isotopes, at least in bold first approximation, as "gases" of noninteracting atoms at the same density as the actual liquids. Perhaps we might suggest that the physical approximation involved is something like the similar attack one makes on the conduction electrons in metals where, as we mentioned earlier (see footnote on p. 88), we may say that the very large zero-point energy of the assembly gives us some justification for treating the electrons as free, noninteracting particles. A He^4 atom is made up in all of six "fundamental particles" (2 protons and 2 neutrons in the nucleus, and there are two extranuclear electrons), each of which has half-integral spin. It therefore turns out that, if we are to treat each He^4 atom as an independent particle, its total spin must be *integral*, and consequently in turn a noninteracting assembly of such He^4 atoms must be regarded as an assembly of independent "bosons," i.e., as a Bose-Einstein gas. On the other hand, if we adopt the same approach for liquid He^3 (the nucleus now having two protons and one neutron), we must regard it as a Fermi-Dirac "gas" at the appropriate density.

3.7.3 Liquid He^4 as a Bose-Einstein "Gaslike" Model

We consider first the behavior to be expected of liquid He^4 at constant density on this basis. We have as usual N particles in a volume V.

* It appears that F. E. Simon (Sir Francis Simon) was one of the first to realize clearly the physical importance of zero-point energy in governing the behavior of liquid helium. Simon used very descriptive expressions such as that "liquid helium is blown up by its own zero point energy."

Then the permissible, and very closely spaced, nonlocalizable energy levels ϵ_i in this gaslike model are given by

$$\epsilon_i = \frac{h^2(\mathfrak{n}_1{}^2 + \mathfrak{n}_2{}^2 + \mathfrak{n}_3{}^2)}{2mV^{2/3}}, \qquad \text{(i.e., Eq. 89}a\text{)} \tag{113}$$

where $\mathfrak{n}_1$, $\mathfrak{n}_2$, and $\mathfrak{n}_3$ are any (positive or negative) integers, and as usual

$$N = \sum_i n_i = \sum_i \frac{g_i}{e^{(\epsilon_i - \mu)/kT} - 1}, \tag{114}$$

where, if we use strictly the energy levels of Eq. 113, $g_i = 1$ throughout.

Whenever possible, however, it is naturally most desirable in analysis to replace summations (which are frequently very difficult to deal with) by integrations, i.e., to replace here g_i by $g(\epsilon)\,d\epsilon$ with an appropriate integration. If we do this, using Eq. 104 for $g(\epsilon)$, we have then

$$N = \frac{2\pi V}{h^3}(2m)^{3/2} \int_0^\infty \frac{\epsilon^{1/2}\,d\epsilon}{e^{(\epsilon-\mu)/kT} - 1}. \tag{115}$$

Now the replacement of such a sum by the corresponding integral is, very roughly speaking, likely to be a fair approximation so long as the finite difference between successive values of the variable is small compared with, or at worst comparable with, the value of the variable itself; i.e., here we would require $\Delta\epsilon \lesssim \epsilon$. This will broadly be true for all the energy levels *except obviously* $\epsilon = 0$. Indeed the integral approximation of Eq. 115 effectively *excludes* the particle state $\epsilon = 0$, because $g(\epsilon)$, $\sim\epsilon^{1/2}$, vanishes for $\epsilon = 0$. Now in a classical gas, or in a Fermi-Dirac gas, the net fraction of particles that could ever be in the state $\epsilon = 0$ is always extremely tiny in comparison with the number in all the other elementary states.* Consequently in these situations the integral approximation using the density of states is always entirely adequate. However, in the Bose-Einstein gas there is no *a priori* restriction on how many particles of the assembly may occupy the lowest (or any) particle state if this is statistically favorable. Thus if a significant fraction of the particles should congregate specifically in the state $\epsilon = 0$, the integral representation of Eq. 115 would then be inadequate. We must thus always "keep a weather

* Because (i), we require in the classical assembly that the relative occupancy number ($f_i \equiv n_i/g_i$) of *any* and *every* state is extremely small ($f_i \ll 1$ for *every* i). (ii), in the Fermi-Dirac assembly the Pauli Principle *restricts* us to a maximum of one particle per elementary state, and hence at most we may only have *one* particle in the lowest particle state (here $\epsilon = 0$), in comparison with perhaps 10^{22} particles in all the other states!

eye open" in Bose-Einstein statistics as to whether we must more strictly include on the right-hand side of Eq. 115 an additional term $1/(e^{-\mu/kT} - 1)$ to allow specifically for the number of particles in the state $\epsilon = 0$ ($\mathfrak{n}_1 = \mathfrak{n}_2 = \mathfrak{n}_3 = 0$ in Eq. 113).

Consider Eq. 115 as it stands. The chemical potential μ in a Bose-Einstein gas can never be positive (i.e., we must have $\mu \leq 0$); and this we can see on the following two grounds:

(1) A positive value of μ at $T = 0$ would mean physically the existence of some zero-point energy of the assembly (as of course exists validly in the Fermi-Dirac gas), but in the Bose-Einstein assembly we have specifically assumed that all particles may ultimately fall into the state $\epsilon = 0$ without restriction, and hence there is no physical reason that would lead to such a zero-point energy.

(2) If, at any temperature, μ were positive, then for some energies, ϵ_i ($\epsilon_i < \mu$), the occupation numbers n_i given by

$$n_i = \frac{g_i}{e^{(\epsilon_i - \mu)/kT} - 1},$$

would become *negative*, and this we reject as physically meaningless.

Now with $\mu \leq 0$, and $\epsilon \geq 0$, the integral in Eq. 115 will have as an upper limit a definite maximum value at any given temperature T if we set $\mu = 0$. With $\mu = 0$ we have then for this maximum value from Eq. 115

$$\frac{N}{V} = \frac{2\pi}{h^3}(2m)^{3/2}\int_0^\infty \frac{\epsilon^{1/2}\,d\epsilon}{e^{\epsilon/kT} - 1}$$
$$= \frac{2\pi}{h^3}(2mkT)^{3/2}\int_0^\infty \frac{x^{1/2}\,dx}{e^x - 1} = \frac{2\pi\eta}{h^3}(2mkT)^{3/2}, \qquad (116)$$

where:

$$\eta \equiv \int_0^\infty \frac{x^{1/2}\,dx}{e^x - 1} = 2.315\ \ldots\,.$$

That is to say, in a Bose-Einstein gas at any particular temperature T there is a maximum density of particles N/V, as given by Eq. 116, which can be found in the totality of states *above* $\epsilon = 0$, (bearing in mind that the integral excludes strictly the state at $\epsilon = 0$). This in turn means that, if we are *given* a certain density N/V for our assembly (for example, the normal density of liquid He^4), then Eq. 116 determines a certain characteristic temperature, $T = T_c$ say, corresponding to that particular density. *Below* T_c as determined by Eq. 116 we must then take specific account of the state $\epsilon = 0$, since below that temperature a substantial fraction of the whole assembly of particles will be in this energy state. *Above* T_c, however, the fraction of particles in the state $\epsilon = 0$ is quite negligible, and we can then use Eq. 115 adequately as it stands to determine numerically the chemical potential μ. As the temperature increases above T_c, μ becomes rapidly more negative, and increases in magnitude monotonically ($\mu \to -\infty$) as the classical distribution is approached at sufficiently high temperatures. *Below* T_c the chemical potential μ remains extremely close to zero, so that in effect the maximum number of particles possible is being accommodated in the higher particle energy states, and the remainder must then congregate in the single state $\epsilon = 0$. The transition at T_c is actually very sharp,* so that the temperature T_c, as determined by Eq. 116, is known as the Bose-Einstein "condensation temperature." Above T_c the state $\epsilon = 0$ is of no real significance, and below T_c we have a progressively greater fraction of all the particles "condensing" into this state. In fact we see from Eq. 116 that this fraction of particles in the ground state, say $\mathcal{f}_0$, for $T \leq T_c$ is

$$\mathcal{f}_0 = 1 - \left(\frac{T}{T_c}\right)^{3/2} \qquad \text{(see Fig. 16).} \tag{117}$$

In other words, below T_c a fraction $(T/T_c)^{3/2}$ of the particles is to be found in the states above $\epsilon = 0$, and very roughly we may say that these particles in "excited" states will have an average thermal energy $\sim kT$ per particle; thus we should expect a molar internal energy below T_c given roughly by

$$E \sim RT\left(\frac{T}{T_c}\right)^{3/2}, \tag{118a}$$

and consequently a specific heat

$$C_V = \left(\frac{\partial E}{\partial T}\right)_V \sim R\left(\frac{T}{T_c}\right)^{3/2}. \tag{119a}$$

More precisely (cf. London, 1938) for $T \leq T_c$ we find

$$E = 0.771RT\left(\frac{T}{T_c}\right)^{3/2}, \tag{118b}$$

* It can be shown (see again London, 1938), that the transition region, say ΔT, is given in order of magnitude by $\Delta T \sim T_c/N$, where N as usual is the total number of particles in the assembly. Obviously then for any macroscopic assembly N is so large that ΔT is *extremely* small.

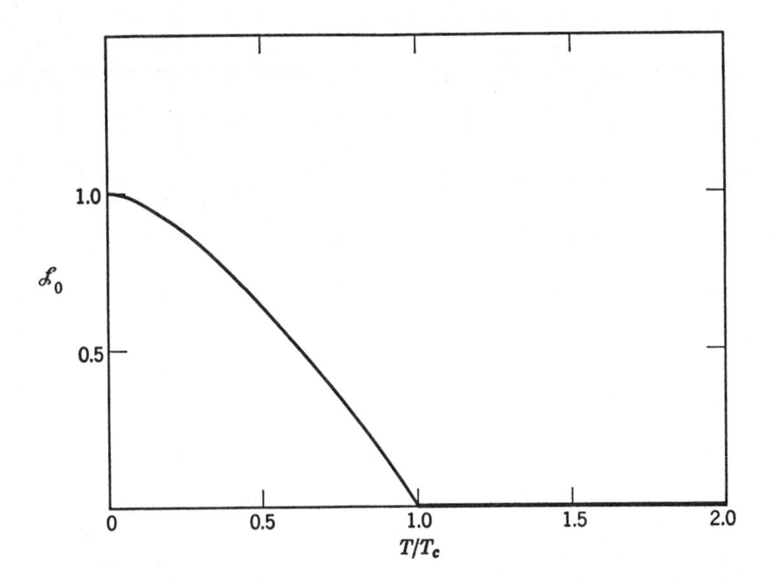

FIG. 16. Fraction of total number of particles occupying lowest particle energy state (i.e., "ground state," $\epsilon = 0$) in the idealized Bose-Einstein "gaslike" assembly. This fraction, say $\mathscr{f}_0$, is given by

$$\mathscr{f}_0 = 1 - (T/T_c)^{3/2} \qquad \text{(Eq. 117)},$$

where T_c is the "Bose-Einstein condensation temperature."

and consequently

$$C_V = \frac{\partial E}{\partial T} = 1.93R\left(\frac{T}{T_c}\right)^{3/2} \tag{119b)*}$$

* Using Eq. 210 of Appendix IV, we can write for the entropy of a Bose-Einstein gas

$$S = -k \int_0^{\infty} \{f(\epsilon) \ln f(\epsilon) - [1 + f(\epsilon)] \ln [1 + f(\epsilon)]\} g(\epsilon)\, d\epsilon, \tag{120}$$

where $f(\epsilon) = 1/(e^{(\epsilon-\mu)/kT} - 1)$, and if we use Eq. 104 for $g(\epsilon)$, Eq. 120 will be valid both above *and* below $T = T_c$. This is so because the particle "ground state" itself ($\epsilon = 0$) will always contribute negligibly to the *entropy*, and hence we make no error in ignoring this state in calculating S. If in Eq. 120, for $T \leq T_c$, we set $\mu \approx 0$, so that $f(\epsilon) = 1/(e^{\epsilon/kT} - 1)$, we see readily that the molar entropy is given by $S \sim R(T/T_c)^{3/2}$; more precisely the theory (cf. London, 1938) for $T \leq T_c$ gives

$$S = 1.285R\left(\frac{T}{T_c}\right)^{3/2}, \tag{121}$$

and thus for $T \leq T_c$

$$C_V = T\frac{\partial S}{\partial T} = 1.93R\left(\frac{T}{T_c}\right)^{3/2}, \tag{121a}$$

in agreement with Eq. 119*b*.

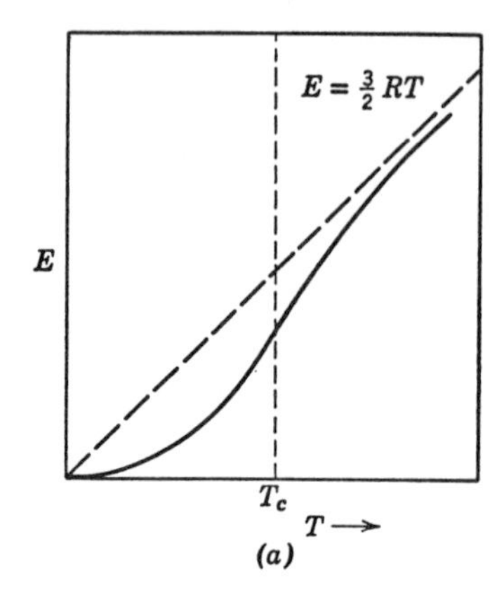

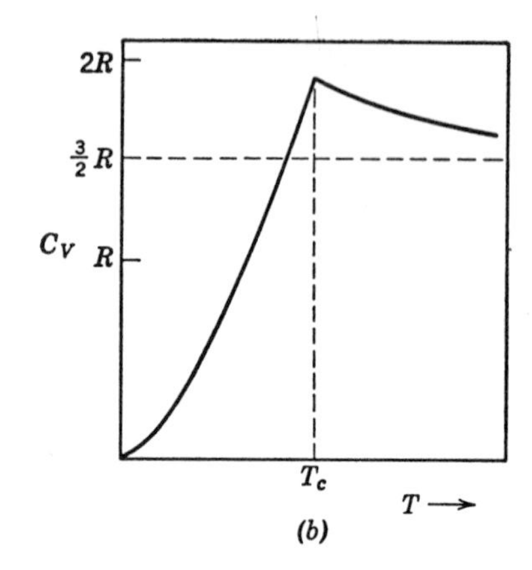

FIG. 17. General thermodynamic behavior of idealized Bose-Einstein "gas."
(*a*) **Rough sketch** of the dependence of the molar internal energy E on temperature. At sufficiently low temperatures ($T < T_c$, where T_c is the Bose-Einstein condensation temperature—see text), $E = 0.77_1 RT(T/T_c)^{\frac{3}{2}}$. At sufficiently high temperatures, E approaches the classical behavior (i.e., $E \approx \frac{3}{2}RT$) indicated by the dashed line.

Obviously at some intermediate temperature (i.e., T_c), the derivative (i.e., $C_V = \partial E/\partial T$) *must* go through a maximum.

(*b*) Dependence of the molar specific heat, C_V, on temperature (after London, 1938). At sufficiently low temperatures ($T < T_c$), $C_V = 1.93R(T/T_c)^{\frac{3}{2}}$. At sufficiently high temperatures, C_V diminishes towards the "classical" limit indicated by the dashed line (i.e., $C_V \approx \frac{3}{2}R$).

Thus at the "condensation temperature" T_c the specific heat at constant volume of a Bose-Einstein gas actually *exceeds* the value for a "classical" gas ($C_V = \frac{3}{2}R$), which, however, must be approached asymptotically at sufficiently high temperatures. In fact C_V shows essentially a cusp* maximum at $T = T_c$, and the general behavior of the internal energy E and the specific heat C_V are shown in Figs. 17*a* and 17*b*. If one has become strongly accustomed to think of the behavior of a "classical" gas as the norm, then the behavior of C_V in a Bose-Einstein gas (and particularly the maximum) seems very anomalous; physicists particularly are inclined to seek for rather special reasons to account for this behavior. Let us note therefore that, first, the existence of a maximum of some kind in C_V is a simple and inevitable consequence of the fact that the energy E in a Bose-Einstein gas must start from zero at $T = 0$ and reach ultimately the classical value $E \approx \frac{3}{2}RT$ (see Fig. 17*a* again; the derivative $\partial E/\partial T = C_V$ must

* See again footnote on p. 102.

obviously go through a maximum at *some* temperature in a Bose-Einstein gas). Secondly, the *cusp* in C_V is a direct consequence of the onset at $T = T_c$ of the "condensation" of particles into the ground state $\epsilon = 0$, which then increases progressively as the temperature is reduced (see again Fig. 16). (For some further discussion of the general behavior, see, e.g., London, 1938; Guénault and MacDonald, 1962.)

3.7.4 Specific Comparison with Liquid He^4

Equation 116 gives for the "condensation temperature"

$$T_c = \left(\frac{\mathfrak{N}}{2.612\mathcal{V}}\right)^{2/3} \frac{h^2}{2\pi mk}, \tag{116a}$$

where $\mathfrak{N}$ is Avogadro's number, $\mathcal{V}$ is the molar volume, and 2.612 is the value of

$$\frac{2}{\sqrt{\pi}} \int_0^\infty \frac{x^{1/2}\,dx}{e^x - 1}.$$

If m is the mass of a He^4 atom ($\sim 7 \times 10^{-24}$ gram), and $\mathcal{V} = 27.6$ cm^3 (the actual molar volume for liquid He^4 just above the experimental "lambda-point" at about 2.2°K; see the following), then Eq. 116*a* predicts $T_c = 3.13$°K. Now the remarkably interesting feature, as London (1938) appreciated, is that liquid He^4 is found *experimentally* to undergo a striking transformation of its physical properties at 2.19°K (under its saturation vapor pressure) as the temperature is lowered from the normal boiling point of about 4.2°K. Perhaps we should notice first and foremost that the experimentally observed specific heat of liquid He^4 exhibits a sharp anomaly with a very steep maximum at 2.19°K (see Fig. 18), and its resemblance to the Greek letter lambda (Λ, λ) leads to this temperature being known as the "lambda-point" for liquid He^4.* Secondly, the closeness of the experi-

* The name "lambda-point" is used rather more generally for sharp specific heat anomalies of this general form, which occur in a number of substances where some transition to a more disordered state on heating culminates at the transition temperature. The generic name "order-disorder transition" is often used.

In a broad sense one would be inclined to say that a transition showing a *latent* heat, such as melting in particular, is the limit of such a process where essentially the whole disordering process occurs "catastrophically" at a single temperature. Generally speaking, however, the term "order-disorder transition" is reserved for transformations where a very substantial part, at least, of the disordering process takes place well before the final transition temperature.

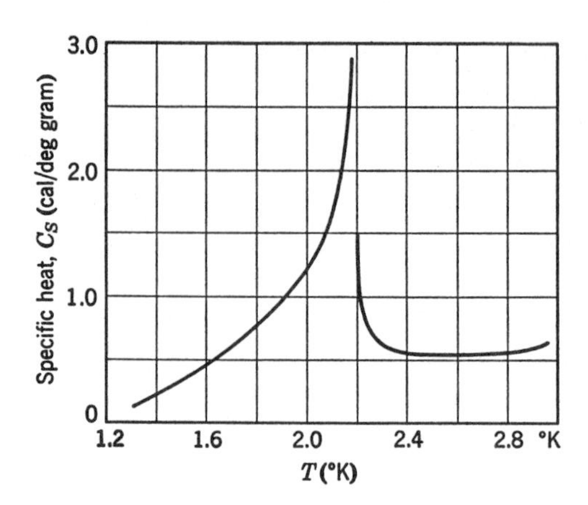

FIG. 18. Experimentally observed specific heat (C_S), under the saturation vapor pressure of liquid He^4 (as reproduced in the review article by Mendelssohn, 1956).
Although the specific heat rises to a very sharp peak at about 2.19°K (the "lambda-point"), careful experimental work shows that there is no *latent heat* associated with the transition (see also Mendelssohn, *loc. cit.*).

mental "lambda-point" (2.19°K) to the theoretical Bose-Einstein condensation temperature (3.13°K) for the gaslike model is striking.

Above this lambda-point, liquid He^4 behaves more or less like a normal liquid, if we bear in mind Simon's general comment that it is "blown up" in volume by its zero-point energy. Below the lambda-point the properties are most remarkable, and have been studied in detail by experimentalists for a number of years (cf., e.g., Mendelssohn, 1956, for a review). The most striking features are that below the lambda-point the liquid behaves under certain circumstances as if its viscosity were vanishingly small (the property of "superfluidity") and also exhibits an extremely high thermal conductivity under appropriate experimental conditions. The change in behavior is so striking that *above* the lambda-point liquid He^4 is generally known (perhaps confusingly) as "liquid He I," and below the lambda-point as "liquid He II."

The two properties of "superfluidity" and "supra thermal conductivity" are undoubtedly intimately related and, broadly speaking, the most useful and rather general semitheoretical description of these properties has rested on a so-called "two-fluid model." The philosophy of the model is that, as we reduce the temperature below the lambda-point, an increasing fraction of the particles or atoms of the liquid goes somehow from a "normal" state to a "superfluid" state, and it is this latter fraction of particles which is supposed to be basically responsible for the anomalous properties. A similar two-fluid model has proved very useful, and often illuminating, for the general description of the superconductive properties observed in many metals at sufficiently low temperatures, where it is correspondingly assumed that below the superconductive transition temperature an increasing fraction of the conduction electrons transfer from "normal" states to some "superconductive" state.

If we try to identify the experimental lambda-point in liquid He^4 with the Bose-Einstein condensation temperature T_c, as F. London specifically proposed, it seems natural then to suggest that the "superfluid" state must be essentially the particle state $\epsilon = 0$ into which, as we have seen, a progressively greater fraction of the "bosons" condense as the temperature is reduced below T_c. We would then identify essentially the "normal" component of liquid He^4 in the two-fluid model as that fraction of He^4 atoms which at any temperature T are in particle states *above* $\epsilon = 0$, and as we have just said, the "superfluid" (and "supra thermal conductive") component of the liquid as that fraction of the He^4 atoms which are specifically in the single particle state $\epsilon = 0$.

We shall not attempt to pursue the problem of liquid He^4 in any further detail here. We must remember that, although the interatomic forces are relatively weak in liquid helium, they are nonetheless present (for if not, we should presumably have no condensed phase at all under normal pressures!), and therefore to use a gaslike model is still a very severe approximation. Various attempts have been made to improve the theoretical models, and we shall close the matter here by referring to a recent review by Feynman (1955), (or see Feynman, 1957).

3.7.5 The Problem of Liquid He^3

If we are at all justified in treating liquid He^4 as a Bose-Einstein gas, then presumably it should be just as valid to treat liquid He^3 as a Fermi-Dirac "gas" in more or less the same approximation. We know, however, already that the specific heat of a Fermi-Dirac gas (cf. Fig. 13) increases smoothly and monotonically from the lowest temperatures (where $C_V \propto T$; cf. Section 3.6.2) until the classical limit ($C_V \approx \frac{3}{2}R$) is approached, and no "anomaly" or sharp transition temperature is to be expected theoretically. Thus if this general approach to liquid helium is justified as a first approximation, we should expect at least that liquid He^3:—

(1) would show *no* "lambda-point" nor any transformation to a "superfluid" (or similar) state with reduction of temperature.

(2) would, below some characteristic temperature, show a specific heat (and an entropy S) which would, as $T \rightarrow 0$, decay towards zero *linearly* with temperature.

It turns out that experimentally these predictions about the behavior of liquid He^3 are indeed fulfilled. No trace has yet been found, even in experiments down to as low as $\sim$0.1°K, of a "superfluid" state* in liquid He^3, and it appears that for temperatures below the order of 0.5°K the entropy and the specific heat of liquid He^3 do decay towards zero linearly with temperature. Much work remains to be done in understanding the *detailed* behavior of liquid He^3, such as accounting for the actual temperature at which the linear decay of entropy sets in.†

However, on the whole it appears rather certain today that it is the difference between the statistical mechanics of assemblies whose wave functions are *symmetric* (He^4), or *antisymmetric* (He^3), which is fundamentally responsible for the remarkable behavior of liquid He^4 and the striking difference in behavior between liquid He^4 and liquid He^3. The difference in atomic mass between the isotopes is certainly far from unimportant, but it appears nonetheless that the symmetry properties play the primary role.

3.8 ELECTROMAGNETIC RADIATION

In dealing with the statistical thermodynamics of electromagnetic radiation, the problem today can be approached in two somewhat different ways. The identity of the answers is an important aspect of electromagnetic theory. The starting point for either approach to the problem is the same: We consider an enclosure of volume V at temperature T, and we wish to determine the equilibrium properties of electromagnetic radiation in that enclosure (in particular the energy density of the radiation and its frequency distribution).

We have first to decide what *frequencies* of electromagnetic radiation are permitted within the enclosure, or in other words the frequency

* However, it appears (cf. Daunt, 1962) that recent theoretical developments today predict that even in liquid He^3 some superfluid state should develop at *very* low temperatures, according to Daunt in the order of 10^{-4} to 10^{-3}°K. It has not yet been possible to examine these predictions experimentally at such extremely low temperatures, but naturally such theoretical proposals provide a keen stimulus for pressing still lower in temperature with appropriate experiments.

† See again Daunt, 1962 for a short review of these questions.

distribution of the "normal modes" of electromagnetic vibration in the enclosure. This problem is very similar to the problem discussed in Chapter 2 when dealing with the normal modes of vibration of a crystalline solid. The equation we are now considering basically is that of the oscillating electric or magnetic field in the enclosure; thus in the interior of the enclosure (presumed to be vacuum) the electric field **E** obeys the wave equation derived by Maxwell

$$\frac{\partial^2 \mathbf{E}}{\partial x^2} + \frac{\partial^2 \mathbf{E}}{\partial y^2} + \frac{\partial^2 \mathbf{E}}{\partial z^2} = \frac{1}{c^2} \frac{\partial^2 \mathbf{E}}{\partial t^2}, \tag{122}$$

where c is the velocity of light in vacuum. In seeking permitted solutions of Eq. 122, for convenience let us again assume as our boundary condition the "Born cyclic condition" applied to a cubic enclosure of side L, and thereafter our analysis will follow very closely our previous work in Chapter 2 with two added comments:

(1) With our boundary conditions, the normal modes of vibration in the enclosure will be such that the vectors **E** and **H** will always be oscillating in the plane perpendicular to the direction of propagation; or in other words we have only to do with *transverse* modes of vibration (of which there will be two distinct modes for each choice of wave vector), and *no* longitudinal modes.

(2)* In the Debye model for the vibrations of a crystalline solid it is *assumed* for convenience that the normal modes of vibration are nondispersive; in the present situation the normal modes are quite strictly nondispersive, since in vacuum c is a fundamental constant. Moreover we know as yet of no upper limit to the permitted frequencies of vibration, and hence there will be no "cut-off" frequency to be considered in the electromagnetic problem.

With these two comments it follows immediately that the number of modes of *electromagnetic* vibration per unit volume of the container, in the small frequency range $d\nu$, is given by

$$d\tilde{\mathsf{N}} = \frac{8\pi\nu^2 \, d\nu}{c^3} \qquad \text{(cf. Eq. 56)}, \tag{123}$$

where now we have a factor 8π and *not* 12π as in Eq. 56, because we have no longitudinal electromagnetic vibrations in our model.

We can now proceed from this point in two rather different ways.

* Historically of course the analysis of the normal modes of electromagnetic vibration *preceded* that of the Debye model for the material vibrations of a solid.

3.8.1 The "Oscillator Model"

We can now assume, exactly as we did in our Debye model for the vibrations of a solid,* that to each of these normal modes of vibration (which are "localizable" (or distinguishable) in wave vector space) we assign a quantum harmonic oscillator with, as usual, energy levels

$$\epsilon_i = (i + \tfrac{1}{2})h\nu, \qquad \text{(cf. Eq. 43 in Chapter 2).}$$

Hence to each mode of vibration of frequency ν corresponds an average energy:

$$<\epsilon> = \frac{h\nu}{2} + \frac{h\nu}{e^{h\nu/kT} - 1}, \qquad \text{(cf. Eq. 47}c\text{).} \tag{124}$$

If now we restrict our attention to the part of the average energy (say $<\epsilon_T>$) which depends explicitly on temperature, we shall ignore the first (zero-point) term,† retaining only

$$<\epsilon_T> = \frac{h\nu}{e^{h\nu/kT} - 1}. \tag{124a}$$

Consequently, in the frequency range $d\nu$, the corresponding energy density $\tilde{E}_\nu$ of equilibrium electromagnetic radiation at temperature T is

$$\tilde{E}_\nu = \frac{h\nu}{e^{h\nu/kT} - 1}\, d\tilde{N} = \frac{8\pi h\nu^3}{c^3(e^{h\nu/kT} - 1)}\, d\nu, \tag{125}$$

when we use Eq. 123 for $d\tilde{N}$. Consequently the over-all energy density of thermally generated electromagnetic radiation in equilibrium at temperature T is given by

$$\tilde{E} = \frac{8\pi h}{c^3}\int_0^\infty \frac{\nu^3\, d\nu}{e^{h\nu/kT} - 1} = \frac{8\pi h}{c^3}\left(\frac{kT}{h}\right)^4 \int_0^\infty \frac{x^3\, dx}{e^x - 1}$$

$$= \frac{8\pi^5 h}{15c^3}\left(\frac{kT}{h}\right)^4. \tag{126}$$

* But bear in mind again that the Debye model actually came later.

† The significance of the first term in Eq. 124 poses quite an embarrassing problem in electromagnetic theory. Coupled with the frequency distribution of Eq. 123, with *no* "cut-off" frequency, it implies an infinite "zero-point" electromagnetic energy per unit volume of space. This sort of problem crops up again and again in different guises, and we can say that we are in effect adopting a so-called renormalization procedure by simply "ignoring" this apparently infinite "zero-point" energy, which is *independent* of temperature, and concerning ourselves only with the temperature-dependent component. But in any case, from the point of view of deducing the net radiative exchange that will take place between a hotter and a colder body we are certainly right in ignoring the "zero-point" energy, but it is worth remembering that this apparently infinite energy poses a fundamental problem in quantum electrodynamics.

Consider now some plane surface of unit area in a region where such equilibrium electromagnetic radiation exists. It can be shown that the average energy which will pass through this surface from one particular side to the other per second, and which then defines the *intensity* of such radiation, say $\mathcal{I}$, is given by

$$\mathcal{I} = \frac{c\tilde{E}}{4};$$

hence

$$\mathcal{I} = \frac{2\pi^5 k^4}{15c^2h^3} T^4, \tag{127}$$

when we use Eq. 126 for $\tilde{E}$. Thus

$$\mathcal{I} = \sigma T^4, \tag{127a}$$

where the constant $\sigma = 2\pi^5 k^4/15c^2h^3$ defines Stefan's constant. One can show quite generally by pure thermodynamic reasoning that the intensity $\mathcal{I}$ must be proportional to T^4 for equilibrium electromagnetic radiation, but we have to invoke statistical mechanics, as we have done, to deduce a specific value for Stefan's constant in terms of the fundamental constants. Perhaps one should remark that the reasoning only applied rigorously to the electromagnetic radiation which is in strict *thermal equilibrium* in some enclosure at temperature T; it is, however, assumed that the foregoing results can be extended to the net radiation which would pass from a hotter body (at temperature T_1) to a colder body (at temperature T_2). If these are so-called "black" bodies, then we assume that the intensity of the radiation leaving *each* body is given by Eq. 127. Thus, for example, if we assume that the sun is a "black" body of surface area A, at temperature T_1, which is surrounded by a universe of "black body temperature" T_2, then it is predicted that the *net* rate of loss $\mathcal{L}$ of electromagnetic radiation from the sun per second would be

$$\mathcal{L} = \sigma A(T_1{}^4 - T_2{}^4), \tag{128}$$

where σ is Stefan's constant as defined in Eq. 127.

Physical bodies will depart in some degree from "perfectly black" bodies, and this departure can be allowed for to some extent in practice by assuming an "equivalent black body temperature," which differs more or less from the physical temperature of the body. However, this will usually be only a partial approximation because the deviation of the radiating surface from perfect "black body" conditions will in general mean that the spectrum of radiation from the body is no longer that calculated in Eq. 125. In other words, a physical body may be "blacker" (i.e., radiate, and absorb, energy more efficiently) in some regions of the electromagnetic spectrum than in others. To deal with this sort of situation in detail would now require us to consider specific atomic models for the electromagnetic properties of particular solids, and we shall not go further here.

3.8.2 The "Photon Model"

There is an alternative description of electromagnetic radiation wherein we postulate that to each of our permitted modes of vibration of frequency ν we have present in our container at temperature T excited quanta of energy $h\nu$ which we can treat to some extent as (indistinguishable) quasi-particles. These quantized energy excitations, or "light-particles," are known of course as "photons." Now to any given oscillator frequency ν_i (and hence a corresponding *photon* energy* $\epsilon_i = h\nu_i$) there is no a priori restriction on the maximum energy of an oscillator, or in other words no restriction on the *number* of (indistinguishable) photons of energy ϵ_i appropriate to that frequency. This then implies that, if we are to treat the radiation in this way as a "gaslike" assembly of "light-particles" or photons, we should use Bose-Einstein statistics for the photons, and it is consistent with what we have said earlier that indeed spectroscopic evidence requires us to regard photons as having integral spins ($0, \hbar, 2\hbar, \ldots$). However, the photons are still sufficiently nonparticle in character that they can be readily created or destroyed; this is perhaps another way of saying that a photon has no *rest mass*. From the point of view of employing statistical mechanics for the problem, this means that we must *not* apply the number-restriction in evaluating the distribution for the photon assembly; i.e., we must *not* apply the usual restriction: $\sum_i n_i = \text{constant}$.† This means that no parameter α will now appear

* Note carefully that in this section, using a photon assembly, we now logically use the symbol ϵ_i to denote the energy of a *photon* (of frequency ν_i). This is to be distinguished from the use of ϵ_i in the previous section, using an oscillator assembly, to denote there the energy levels of an *oscillator*.

† It seems important to realize how vital the "restrictive conditions" of statistical mechanics are. The condition $\sum_i n_i\epsilon_i = E$ not only means that we are specifying that the over-all energy in an isolated "container" must be constant (in technical language we are dealing strictly with a so-called "micro-canonical ensemble"), but also it postulates in effect that energy *can* be readily exchanged between the various elements of the assembly. It is precisely this condition that involves the very concept of a thermal equilibrium being possible in an assembly. It is then very natural that the temperature T *enters* via this condition, because physically

in the equation for Bose-Einstein statistics (cf. Appendix III and Eq. 94) when applied to photons, so that we have simply:

$$n_i = \frac{g_i}{e^{\epsilon_i/kT} - 1}. \tag{129}$$

If we consider the group of vibrations in the small frequency interval $d\nu$, all having practically the same frequency ν and hence the same photon energy $h\nu$, then for the photon assembly

$$\epsilon_i = h\nu, \tag{130}$$

and we have for unit volume

$$g_i = \frac{8\pi\nu^2\, d\nu}{c^3}, \qquad \text{(cf. Eq. 123).} \tag{131}$$

The most probable number of photons (n_i) per unit volume in the frequency interval $d\nu$, at temperature T, is given by Eqs. 129, 130, and 131; let us write for convenience $d\tilde{n} = n_i$, so that we have

$$d\tilde{n} = \frac{8\pi\nu^2\, d\nu}{c^3(e^{h\nu/kT} - 1)}. \tag{132}$$

Since to each of these photons corresponds an *energy* $h\nu$, the excitation energy per unit volume of electromagnetic radiation in the frequency interval $d\nu$, is

$$h\nu \cdot d\tilde{n} = \tilde{E}_\nu = \frac{8\pi\nu^2 h\nu\, d\nu}{c^3(e^{h\nu/kT} - 1)}. \tag{133}$$

This result is in precise agreement with Eq. 125, thus demonstrating the satisfying equivalence of the two approaches to the problem.

---

speaking if two parts of our assembly are at different temperatures, then energy transfer ("heat conduction") will take place until the two parts of our assembly have reached the same temperature; in other words, the assembly has achieved over-all thermal equilibrium at a single temperature T.

The second restrictive condition (i.e., $\sum_i n_i = N$ for our assemblies of "particles") specifies precisely what we *mean* by talking about "particles" or "atoms" in statistical mechanics; namely that they may be found in different "states" from time to time, but they have certain vital features which are *conserved* at all times, so that the total number N remains constant.

Perhaps the most remarkable point is that such fundamental physical information is expressed in these two apparently very simple "restrictive" conditions.

4

CLASSICAL STATISTICAL MECHANICS

4.1 THE GENERAL TRANSITION TO CLASSICAL MECHANICS

We have already seen on various occasions that limiting situations of one kind or another have led to well-known classical expressions for the energy or entropy of some thermodynamic system. Thus when dealing with crystalline solids on either the Einstein or Debye model, we found that the lattice vibrations could be characterized in first approximation by some particular frequency, or by an equivalent characteristic temperature θ, and in general θ was explicitly involved in expressions for the energy E or in other thermodynamic quantities. When $T \gtrsim \theta$, however, we saw that the molar energy was given quite simply by $E \approx 3RT$, and correspondingly the specific heat by $C_V \approx 3R$. These latter results, agreeing with the so-called Dulong-Petit Law for the molar specific heats of solids, correspond to the classical result for a harmonic solid that to each position and momentum coordinate we may assign a thermal energy $kT/2$. Or again, when dealing with the ideal gas, we arrived at an equation of state $p\mathcal{V} = RT$ (where $\mathcal{V}$ is the molar volume), a molar energy $E = \frac{3}{2}RT$, and a specific heat $C_V = 3R/2$, all of which could also have been derived from a so-called classical treatment, i.e., where the analysis is based directly on Newtonian or classical dynamics from the start. We note in particular that the molar energy for the perfect gas would again correspond to assuming an energy $kT/2$ per degree of freedom, since only kinetic energy, depending on the momenta of the gas particles, is now involved.

We may therefore well ask whether there is any *general* formulation of the results of statistical mechanics which we could use immediately for problems in which we believed that a description by purely classical mechanics would suffice at the particle, or "microscopic," level. This can indeed be done, and the expressions are extremely useful and can be applied validly to a remarkably wide range of problems. One should perhaps remark now that in fact statistical mechanics developed *historically* from a classical formulation (naturally enough!), and only later did it assume the form with which we are here familiar (cf. also Sections 1.2.1, 1.2.2, et seq.). However, it is more straightforward, and less confusing in the end, to start from an essentially quantum formulation (as we have done, following Rushbrooke's lead in particular), and then to regard classical statistical mechanics, despite its remarkably wide range of application, as a limiting form of quantum statistical mechanics. The argument that follows, outlining the transition, is far from rigorous, and should be regarded as essentially heuristic and sketchy.

We recall our partition function per particle Z for a system of independent particles

$$Z = \sum_i e^{-\epsilon_i/kT}, \tag{134}$$

where (1) we are summing over all the permissible quantum mechanical states of an element in the assembly, and (2) for convenience here, we assume that the states are nondegenerate.

Now an essential feature of classical mechanics is that the displacement and momentum of a particle are treated as ideal *continuous* variables, in contrast to quantum mechanics. One way of expressing this contrast is through Heisenberg's Uncertainty Principle

$$\Delta x \cdot \Delta p_x \approx h, \tag{135}$$

which one can interpret by saying that "neighboring" quantum states, expressed in the (classical) variables x and p_x, will always be separated from one another in such a way that each quantum state requires a minimum "volume" h in the "space" defined by the variables x and p_x. Going to the limit of classical mechanics implies that the spacing of neighboring quantum levels may be regarded as vanishingly small, and consequently that we should be able to replace the summation in Eq. 134 by an integration. The requirements for replacing a summation by an integration then suggest immediately that, for an integral to be an adequate approximation, the function $e^{-\epsilon/kT}$ must change very little in going from one quantum level to the next, i.e., $\Delta\epsilon/kT \ll 1$.

Let us assume for the present that our system is one-dimensional and that the energy of an element or particle can be expressed in classical (Newtonian) mechanics as a function of x and p_x. We therefore might expect that, in the classical limit, we should be able to write

$$Z = C\iint e^{-\epsilon(p_x,x)/kT}\,dp_x\,dx, \tag{136}$$

where (1) C is some constant yet to be determined to make Z in Eq. 136 agree numerically in the classical limit with Z in Eq. 134, and (2) the integration is to be carried over all permitted values of p_x and x, as determined essentially by the boundary conditions on the assembly.

Now consider say three neighboring (and nondegenerate) quantum states 1, 2, and 3; from Eq. 134 these would contribute to Z

$$Z = e^{-\epsilon_1/kT} + e^{-\epsilon_2/kT} + e^{-\epsilon_3/kT}, \tag{137a}$$

whereas from Eq. 136 we have correspondingly

$$Z \approx Ce^{-\epsilon_1/kT}(\delta p_x\,\delta x)_1 + Ce^{-\epsilon_2/kT}(\delta p_x\,\delta x)_2 + Ce^{-\epsilon_3/kT}(\delta p_x\,\delta x)_3, \tag{137b}$$

where $(\delta p_x\,\delta x)_1$ is the *small* contribution to the range of the integral appropriate to the quantum state 1, etc. But now, bearing in mind the interpretation of Heinsenberg's Uncertainty Principle (Eq. 135) outlined previously, let us write

$$(\delta p_x\,\delta x)_1 = (\delta p_x\,\delta x)_2 = \cdots \approx h. \tag{138}$$

Thus comparing Eqs. 137*a* and 137*b*, we set $C = 1/h$, and hence we are finally led to expect that, in the classical limit of statistical mechanics, we may write for the partition function (per element) for independent elements

$$Z = \frac{1}{h}\iint e^{-\epsilon(p_x,x)/kT}\,dp_x\,dx; \tag{139a}$$

or, more generally, if n independent space variables $(x, y, z, \ldots)$ are necessary in defining the classical energy of a particle in the assembly, we have

$$\boxed{Z = \frac{1}{h^n}\iint \cdots \iint e^{-\epsilon(p_x,p_y,p_z\cdots x,y,z\cdots)/kT}\,dp_x\,dp_y\,dp_z \cdots dx\,dy\,dz \cdots}. \tag{139b*}$$

* We repeat that the approach to Eq. 139*b* is far from rigorous. The historical approach to statistical mechanics involves fundamentally the concept of "phase space" determined by the set of generalized space variables involved (e.g., x, y, z; or r, θ, ϕ, etc.), together with their "conjugate momentum variables." With conventional Cartesian coordinates, x, y, and z, the conjugate momentum variables are simply the familiar Newtonian components of momentum. With more general space variables one must turn to the Lagrangian to determine the

4.1.1 The Ideal Gas

Let us immediately check this expression for the classical partition function. Let us consider, as we did in Chapter 2, a gas of N non-interacting, nonlocalized particles, each of mass m, confined to a cubic container of side L, but without other potential energy. Classically the energy of any particle will be given by

$$\epsilon = \frac{p_x^2}{2m} + \frac{p_y^2}{2m} + \frac{p_z^2}{2m}. \tag{140}$$

Consequently from Eq. 139*b* we have

$$Z = \frac{1}{h^3}\int \cdots \int e^{-(p_x^2+p_y^2+p_z^2)/2mkT}\, dp_x\, dp_y\, dp_z\, dx\, dy\, dz, \tag{141}$$

where, on the one hand, the limits of integration on x, y, and z are each 0 to L since the particles are strictly confined to the container, and, on the other hand, there are no restrictions on the momentum variables. Hence we have

$$Z = \frac{L^3}{h^3}\left\{\int_{-\infty}^{+\infty} e^{-u^2/2mkT}\, du\right\}^3, \tag{141a}$$

writing u for any of the momentum variables. Thus

$$Z = V\frac{(2\pi mkT)^{3/2}}{h^3}, \tag{141b}$$

where V $(= L^3)$ is the volume of the container, and we have again used the well-known result that

$$\int_{-\infty}^{+\infty} e^{-t^2}\, dt = \sqrt{\pi}. \tag{142}$$

We see to our satisfaction that Eq. 141*b* is indeed identical with Eq. 90*c* previously derived in Chapter 3 for the partition function of a particle in an ideal gas.

4.1.2 Assembly of Classical Harmonic Oscillators

Consider now an assembly of $3N$ independent simple oscillators; let the rth oscillator be characterized by displacement coordinate x_r,

---

appropriate conjugate momenta. For spherical polar coordinates (r, θ, and ϕ): $p_r = m\dot{r}$; $p_\theta = mr^2\dot{\theta}$; $p_\phi = mr^2 \sin^2\theta\dot{\phi}$; and for cylindrical polar coodinates (ρ, ϕ, and z): $p_\rho = m\dot{\rho}$; $p_\phi = m\rho^2\dot{\phi}$; $p_z = m\dot{z}$.

We shall, however, use here only the familiar Cartesian coordinates.

conjugate momentum p_r, mass m_r, and frequency ν_r. If we assume all the masses to be identical, i.e., $m_r = m$ say, and likewise treat all the frequencies as identical, i.e., $\nu_r = \nu_E$ say, we have essentially the Einstein model for the vibrations of a crystalline solid (cf. Section 2.2). Alternatively, the frequencies ν_r might be distributed according to a Debye spectrum or according to some more arbitrary distribution, derived from the analysis of the normal modes of vibration of a particular solid. The energy of the rth harmonic oscillator is given in classical mechanics by

$$\epsilon(p_r, x_r) = \frac{p_r^{\,2}}{2m_r} + 2\pi^2 m_r^{\,2} \nu_r^{\,2} x_r^{\,2}, \tag{143}$$

and p_r and x_r are unrestricted. Thus, from Eq. 139*a*, the classical partition function (*per oscillator*) is

$$Z = \frac{1}{h} \int_{x_r=-\infty}^{+\infty} \int_{p_r=-\infty}^{+\infty} e^{-(p_r^2/2m_r + 2\pi_r^2 m_r^2 \nu_r^2 x_r^2)/kT}\, dp_r\, dx_r \tag{144a}$$

$$= \frac{kT}{h\nu_r}, \tag{144b}$$

where we use (twice) Eq. 142.

Now consider Eq. 44, Chapter 2, for the partition function per harmonic oscillator of frequency ν_r derived on the basis of quantum mechanical energy levels, i.e.,

$$Z = \frac{e^{-h\nu_r/2kT}}{1 - e^{-h\nu_r/kT}}. \tag{44}$$

This expression indeed reduces to Eq. 144*b* in the limit $kT/h\nu_r \gg 1$; or, in other words, if we define a characteristic temperature θ_r by writing $h\nu_r = k\theta_r$, the classical limit is reached whenever $T/\theta_r \gg 1$. Thus we confirm again in the classical limit the validity of the integral expression, Eq. 139*b*, for the partition function Z. Using Eq. 144*b* for Z we obtain immediately for the molar energy of the assembly of harmonic oscillators

$$E = \frac{3RT^2}{Z}\left(\frac{\partial Z}{\partial T}\right) = 3RT, \tag{145}$$

(we use Eq. 21*b*, bearing in mind that Z is the partition function per *oscillator*, and we assume $3\mathfrak{N}$ oscillators per mole). Equation 145 is then of course the well-known expression for the internal energy in the classical limit.

If we calculate the molar entropy S of the oscillator assembly (using

Eq. 22b), we have

$$S = \sum_{r=1}^{3\mathfrak{N}} k \ln \frac{T}{\theta_r} + 3R. \tag{146}$$

Writing $\theta_r = \theta_E$ for all r (i.e., using now specifically the Einstein model), we have

$$S = 3R\left(\ln \frac{T}{\theta_E} + 1\right), \tag{146a}$$

which agrees with Eq. 46b in Chapter 2, and was shown to be valid for $T/\theta_E \gg 1$. However, if we attempted to use Eq. 146a (which we derived directly from classical statistical mechanics) at "low" temperatures ($T/\theta_E \ll 1$), we see that S would then apparently diverge to minus infinity. This again illustrates the well-known principle in statistical mechanics that at sufficiently low temperatures classical mechanics must ultimately fail as an adequate description, and in particular it appears that we must always appeal finally to a quantum mechanical description if we are to satisfy the requirements of the Third Law of Thermodynamics* (e.g., in this particular case the requirement that the vibrational entropy of a crystalline solid must tend to zero as $T \to 0$).

4.1.3 Physical Interpretation of Classical Statistical Mechanics

From Eq. 139b we can show readily that the internal energy E of an assembly of N independent particles can be written

* This point is also borne out if we look at the expression for the entropy of an ideal gas (Eq. 91) derived in Chapter 3 (and which would follow again here from Eq. 141b derived *directly* from classical statistical mechanics, since the partition function per particle obtained in this way is identical with that obtained in Chapter 3). We have for the molar entropy:

$$S = R\left(\frac{3}{2}\ln\left(\frac{2\pi mkT}{h^2}\right) - \ln\left(\frac{\mathfrak{N}}{\mathfrak{V}}\right) + \frac{5}{2}\right) \qquad \text{(Eq. 91 in Chapter 3).}$$

This expression for S would ultimately diverge (at least for any given density) at *some* sufficiently low temperature, and this again reflects the fact that, generally speaking, any gaslike assembly which exists significantly at low enough temperatures must then be treated more appropriately either by Fermi-Dirac statistics or Bose-Einstein statistics. This of course we have done when discussing conduction electrons in metals and liquid helium at low temperatures, both on the basis of gaslike assemblies. In both these situations we then have $S \to 0$ as $T \to 0$; in the former, $S \propto T$, and in the latter $S \propto T^{3/2}$ below the Bose-Einstein "condensation temperature."

$$\frac{E}{N} = \frac{\int \cdots \int \epsilon e^{-\epsilon/kT}\,\mathbf{dp}\,\mathbf{dx}}{\int \cdots \int e^{-\epsilon/kT}\,\mathbf{dp}\,\mathbf{dx}}, \qquad \text{(cf. also Eq. 25 in Chapter 1);} \tag{147}$$

(where for convenience we have written $\mathbf{dx} = dx\,dy\,dz\ \ldots$, and similarly for the conjugate momentum coordinates). Equation 147 means physically that in an assembly in equilibrium at temperature T obeying classical mechanics the over-all probability, say δP, of any arbitrary particle having positional coordinates lying in the elementary interval $\mathbf{dx}$ (i.e., in the range x to $x + dx$, y to $y + dy$, etc.), and having momentum coordinates in the elementary interval $\mathbf{dp}$, is given by

$$\boxed{\delta P = \frac{e^{-\epsilon/kT}\,\mathbf{dp}\,\mathbf{dx}}{\int \cdots \int e^{-\epsilon/kT}\,\mathbf{dp}\,\mathbf{dx}}}. \tag{148}$$

4.2 THE MAXWELL-BOLTZMANN DISTRIBUTION

Consider now a classical gas where we assume that a particle, atom, or molecule, has as usual translational kinetic energy:

$$\epsilon_{\text{kin}} = \frac{p_x^2 + p_y^2 + p_z^2}{2m} = \frac{m(v_x^2 + v_y^2 + v_z^2)}{2}$$

and a potential energy, if any, which is a function *only* of the spatial coordinates. From Eq. 148 we have then that the probability, say,

$$P(v_x, v_y, v_z)\,dv_x\,dv_y\,dv_z \equiv P(\mathbf{v})\,\mathbf{dv},$$

that any particular particle has a velocity lying in the range v_x to $v_x + dv_x$, etc., is

$$P(\mathbf{v})\,\mathbf{dv} = \frac{e^{-m(v_x^2+v_y^2+v_z^2)/2kT}\,\mathbf{dv}}{\iiint e^{-m(v_x^2+v_y^2+v_z^2)/2kT}\,\mathbf{dv}},$$

since the integrals involving the spatial coordinates, whatever value they may have, cancel out from numerator and denominator. That is,

$$P(\mathbf{v})\,\mathbf{dv} = \left(\frac{m}{2\pi kT}\right)^{3/2} e^{-m(v_x^2+v_y^2+v_z^2)/2kT}\,\mathbf{dv} \tag{149a}$$

$$= \left(\frac{m}{2\pi kT}\right)^{1/2} e^{-mv_x^2/2kT}\,dv_x \cdot \left(\frac{m}{2\pi kT}\right)^{1/2} e^{-mv_y^2/2kT}\,dv_y \cdot \left(\frac{m}{2\pi kT}\right)^{1/2} e^{-mv_z^2/2kT}\,dv_z. \tag{149b}$$

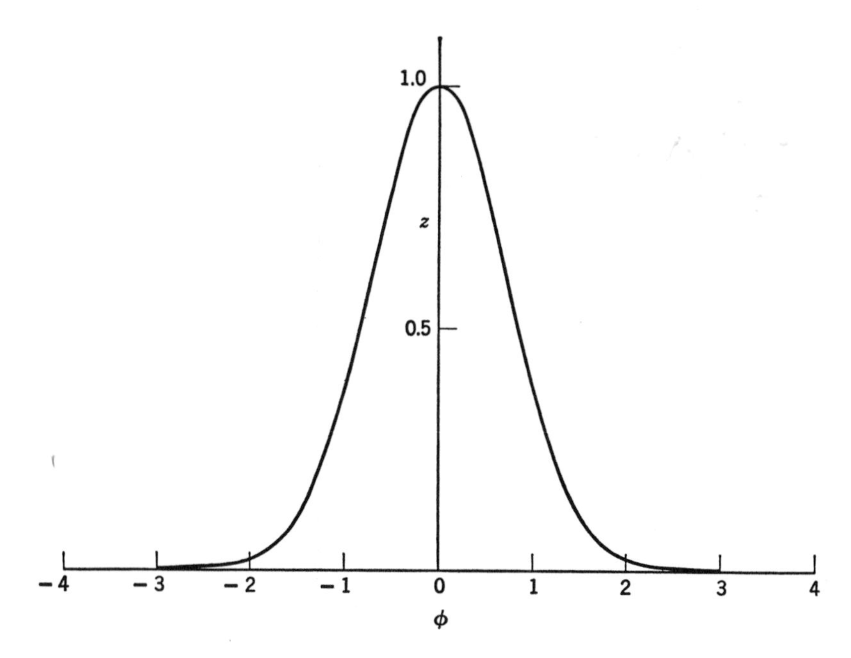

FIG. 19. To illustrate the Maxwell-Boltzmann distribution for a velocity component (say v_x) of a gas molecule. The curve shown is the Gaussian curve $z = e^{-\phi^2}$, and the Maxwell-Boltzmann distribution for velocity follows if we write

$$z = \left(\frac{2\pi kT}{m}\right)^{1/2} P(v_x),$$

where $P(v_x)$ is the probability density, and write

$$\phi = \left(\frac{m}{2kT}\right)^{1/2} v_x.$$

As usual, m is the mass of a gas molecule and T is the absolute temperature.

The final separation of the probability distribution into a product, as in Eq. 149*b*, means that we can write for the probability distribution of any *individual* component of velocity, say v_x, with respect to a fixed axis in space:

$$P(v_x)\, dv_x = \left(\frac{m}{2\pi kT}\right)^{1/2} e^{-mv_x^2/2kT}\, dv_x; \tag{150}$$

i.e., the probability distribution for any particular velocity component that we care to select is given by the well-known Gaussian curve, as illustrated in Fig. 19. Consequently if we ask about the probability distribution of velocity with respect to any particular Cartesian axis (say the x-axis), the distribution is entirely symmetrical in v_x, and therefore such that $\langle v_x \rangle$ is zero, i.e.,

$$\langle v_x \rangle = \int_{-\infty}^{+\infty} v_x P(v_x)\, dv_x = \left(\frac{m}{2\pi kT}\right)^{1/2} \int_{-\infty}^{+\infty} v_x e^{-mv_x^2/2kT}\, dv_x = 0, \tag{151}$$

and the mean square velocity component, say $\langle v_x^2 \rangle$, is given by

$$\langle v_x^2 \rangle = \int_{-\infty}^{+\infty} v_x^2 P(v_x)\, dv_x = \frac{kT}{m}, \tag{152}$$

where we use the result that $\int_{-\infty}^{+\infty} t^2 e^{-t^2}\, dt = \frac{\sqrt{\pi}}{2}$.

We can rewrite Eq. 152 as

$$\tfrac{1}{2}m\langle v_x^2 \rangle = \tfrac{1}{2}kT, \tag{153}$$

which illustrates directly the classical "equipartition principle" of energy. Various other velocity averages may readily be derived, but we shall not pursue this further here since these details belong more properly to the kinetic theory of gases.

4.3 THE ISOTHERMAL EQUILIBRIUM ATMOSPHERE

Another typical problem in classical statistical mechanics is to inquire about the relative change of density of an ideal gaseous atmosphere of particles of mass m, which are in statistical equilibrium at temperature T under a uniform gravitational field (usually that of the earth). Let us assume that the gravitational field acts along the z-axis such that the Newtonian acceleration due to the gravitational field is $-g$ (i.e., we take the z-axis "upwards" from the surface of a plane earth and ignore any variation in g). The kinetic energy of a particle will be as usual $\epsilon_{\text{kin}} = (p_x^2 + p_y^2 + p_z^2)/2m$, and the potential energy of a particle with coordinate z measured from $z = 0$ will be $\epsilon_{\text{pot}} = mgz$. Hence, using Eq. 148, we have for the probability, say $P(z)\, dz$, of finding a particle with its z-coordinate in the range z to $z + dz$

$$P(z)\, dz = \frac{e^{-mgz/kT}\, dz}{\int_0^{\infty} e^{-mgz/kT}\, dz}, \tag{154}$$

since the various other integrations (and in particular those over the momentum variables) cancel out from numerator and denominator.

Equation 154 in turn means that the relative probability of finding a particle in unit spatial volume at height z to that of finding it in unit volume at $z = 0$ is given by

$$\frac{P(z)}{P(0)} = e^{-mgz/kT}. \tag{155a}$$

In other words, if the density of particles at $z = 0$ is ρ_0, the density at height z is given by

$$\boxed{\rho(z) = \rho_0 e^{-mgz/kT}}. \tag{155b}$$

This expression then gives the decay with height z of the density in an ideal isothermal atmosphere in equilibrium at temperature T. One should perhaps notice, as a rather trivial check of this equation, that when $z = 0$, $\rho(z) = \rho_0$ (as we should expect!), and at very great height ($z \rightarrow \infty$), $\rho(z) \rightarrow 0$, also a physically satisfying result. Equation 155b predicts more specifically that the density of the atmosphere will have diminished markedly on reaching a height $\tilde{z} \approx kT/mg$. For $m \approx 5 \times 10^{-23}$ gram (somewhere around the mass of a typical air molecule), and $T \approx 3 \times 10^2$ °K, we have $\tilde{z} \approx 10$ km.

4.4 ASSEMBLY OF ANHARMONIC OSCILLATORS

Consider an (Einstein) assembly of strictly harmonic oscillators all of the same frequency ν and the same mass m, such that for any given oscillator (say the rth) the energy is given by

$$\epsilon = \frac{p_r^2}{2m} + 2\pi^2 m\nu^2 x_r^2, \tag{156}$$

where x_r is the net displacement. Then the *average* net displacement say $\langle x_r \rangle$, for any particular oscillator, is given by

$$\langle x_r \rangle = \frac{\int_{-\infty}^{+\infty} x_r e^{-2\pi^2 m\nu^2 x_r^2/kT}\, dx_r}{\int_{-\infty}^{+\infty} e^{-2\pi^2 m\nu^2 x_r^2/kT}\, dx_r} = 0, \qquad \text{for any temperature } T. \tag{157}$$

If we use this Einstein oscillator model to represent the vibrations of a crystalline solid with free surfaces, it is natural as a *first* approximation to regard any average net displacement of the oscillators (i.e., $\langle x_r \rangle$) as implying a corresponding average net displacement of the atoms of the solid. The fact then that the average oscillator displace-

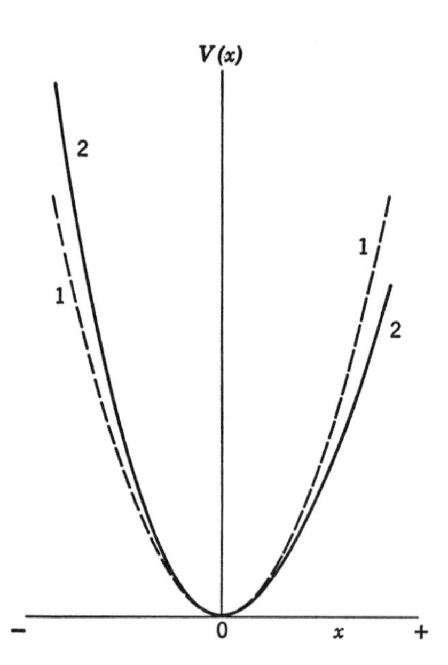

FIG. 20. Rough sketch to illustrate harmonic potential, and modification arising from small cubic anharmonic component.

Curve 1: (Broken curve) Ideal harmonic potential energy curve; i.e., $V(x) = Ax^2$, where A is a constant and x is some appropriate displacement coordinate measured from equilibrium.

Curve 2: (Full curve) Modified potential curve with modest anharmonicity present. This curve might be given by $V(x) = Ax^2 - \lambda x^3$, so long as $|\lambda x^3|$ is small compared with Ax^2.

Note: Roughly speaking, we tend to think of the anharmonic curve as representing crudely the physical situation that when atoms are "pushed together" ($x < 0$) the potential energy rises more sharply than if they are "pulled apart" ($x > 0$). In the same fashion we regard $<x>$ as representing a net thermal expansion in the model.

ment remains zero at all temperatures reflects the argument of Section 1.5.1 that in a crystalline solid with a strictly symmetrical interatomic potential we should expect no thermal expansion.*

Now let us assume that the potential energy of an oscillator is no longer perfectly harmonic, but rather that, in place of Eq. 156

$$\epsilon = \frac{p_r^{\,2}}{2m} + 2\pi^2 m\nu^2 x_r^{\,2} - \lambda x_r^{\,3}, \tag{158}$$

* At least to a first approximation; we have already pointed out that, when dealing with a *real* three-dimensional solid, the definition of a "purely harmonic" solid is more difficult (see footnote on p. 58). We shall, however, ignore this complication in what follows.

where λ is a "small" quantity. In other words, the potential energy increases somewhat less steeply for $x_r > 0$, and more steeply for $x_r < 0$, than in the strictly harmonic model (see Fig. 20 and caption). We have then for the average net displacement $<x_r>$ of an oscillator

$$<x_r> = \frac{\int_{-\infty}^{+\infty} x_r e^{-(2\pi^2 m\nu^2 x_r^2 - \lambda x_r^3)/kT}\, dx_r}{\int_{-\infty}^{+\infty} e^{-(2\pi^2 m\nu^2 x_r^2 - \lambda x_r^3)/kT}\, dx_r}; \qquad (159)$$

and let us now omit for convenience the subscript r. If we assume that the exponential factor $e^{+\lambda x^3/kT}$ may always be treated as close to unity in these integrals so that we may write*

$$e^{+\lambda x\ /kT} \approx 1 + \frac{\lambda x^3}{kT},$$

we have

$$<x> = \frac{\int_{-\infty}^{+\infty} \left(x + \frac{\lambda x^4}{kT}\right) e^{-2\pi^2 m\nu^2 x^2/kT}\, dx}{\int_{-\infty}^{+\infty} e^{-2\pi^2 m\nu^2 x^2/kT}\, dx}. \qquad (160a)$$

that is,

$$<x> = \frac{\lambda kT}{4\pi^4\nu^4 m^2} \frac{\int_{-\infty}^{+\infty} t^4 e^{-t^2}\, dt}{\int_{-\infty}^{+\infty} e^{-t^2}\, dt} = \frac{3\lambda kT}{16\pi^4\nu^4 m^2}, \qquad (160b)$$

where we have used the result that $\int_{-\infty}^{+\infty} t^4 e^{-t^2}\, dt = \frac{3}{4}\sqrt{\pi}$.

From Eq. 160*b* we note first immediately that if $\lambda = 0$ (i.e., a strictly harmonic potential in our model), then $<x> = 0$, which, as before, we interpret as indicating no thermal expansion. Secondly, the net linear expansion as determined by $<x>$ on our model is directly proportional to T, or in other words the predicted expansion coefficient ($\propto \partial<x>/\partial T$) is a constant. In fact, one can show in more detail that the Grüneisen anharmonicity parameter γ (cf. Section 2.5.2)

* Strictly speaking, as they stand, the integrals in Eq. 159 will not converge since, as $x \to +\infty$, $e^{+\lambda x^3/kT}$ would *ultimately* tend to infinity, however small λ may be. When we replace this exponential factor by the terminated expansion $1 + \lambda x^3/kT$, in which case the corresponding integrals in Eq. 160*a* do now converge happily, we are expressing the basic physical assumption that the anharmonic part of the potential is *always* to be regarded as "small."

This model of an anharmonic solid, which has been used in effect by a number of workers in the past, can be criticized on various grounds (cf., e.g., Dugdale and MacDonald, 1954, who analyzed in detail a somewhat more realistic model in one dimension). We only wish here, however, to use the model to illustrate the broad essentials, and for this purpose it is sufficient.

would be on our model directly proportional to the coefficient λ of the anharmonic potential term. The constancy of the predicted thermal expansion coefficient on the foregoing model based on *classical* statistics, together with the direct proportionality of the thermal expansion coefficient to λ (and therefore to γ), agrees with the conclusions in Chapter 2 based on the Grüneisen approach;* in particular that at "high" (classical) temperatures the thermal expansion coefficient is constant.

4.4.1 Anharmonic Correction to Lattice Specific Heat

On this same model and with the same provisos, the average energy per oscillator, say $<\epsilon>$, is given by

$$<\epsilon> = \frac{\iint \epsilon(p, x) e^{-\epsilon(p,x)/kT}\, dp\, dx}{\iint e^{-\epsilon(p,x)/kT}\, dp\, dx} \tag{161}$$

with $\epsilon(p, x)$ in the integrals as given by Eq. 158. This, with our approximations and up to the term in T^2, leads to

$$<\epsilon> = kT + \frac{15}{128} \frac{k^2\lambda^2}{\pi^6 m^3 \nu^6} T^2. \tag{162}$$ †

In other words, on this model the molar internal energy E of an assembly of $3\mathfrak{N}$ slightly anharmonic oscillators would be given by

$$E = 3RT\left(1 + \frac{15}{128} \frac{\lambda^2 kT}{\pi^6 m^3 \nu^6}\right), \tag{163}$$

and therefore for the molar specific heat we have

$$C_V = \frac{\partial E}{\partial T} = 3R\left(1 + \frac{15}{64} \frac{\lambda^2 kT}{\pi^6 m^2 \nu^6}\right). \tag{164}$$

It is interesting to notice that the model predicts that the anharmonicity will contribute, to a first approximation, a "correction" term *linear in* T to the familiar classical specific heat ($C_V = 3R$). This prediction regarding anharmonic effects is at best only valid for classical conditions, i.e., for $T \gtrsim \theta$. We have seen in Chapter 3

* In fact (cf. again Dugdale and MacDonald, 1954; also MacDonald and Roy, 1955) one can show on the model of a linear chain that the agreement is in that case quite precise.

† Compare also Born and Göppert-Mayer, 1933; Born points out there that any quartic term ($\sim x^4$) in the potential will *also* contribute a term in T^2 to the energy.

that we might expect the conduction electrons in metals to contribute at all reasonable temperatures a specific heat which is also linear in T; it might therefore be difficult at normal temperatures to distinguish with any confidence between the contribution to the specific heat from lattice anharmonicity and from the conduction electrons. However, at sufficiently *low* temperatures, as shown previously, the lattice vibrational specific heat must decay to zero very rapidly (and this applies *a fortiori* to any *anharmonic* contribution); it therefore remains true, as pointed out in Section 3.6.3, (see also Fig. 14) that at *sufficiently* low temperatures, and typically below about 10°K, we should be able to pick out experimentally with confidence the electronic specific heat by its continuing linear dependence on temperature, which on the idealized Fermi-Dirac gas model should persist down to absolute zero.

Any more serious attempt than the foregoing to discuss the statistical mechanics of an atomic lattice, taking into account an anharmonic potential, becomes rapidly very much more complex;* we shall therefore leave the question at this point.

4.5 THE PROBLEM OF IRREVERSIBLE PROCESSES

The so-called problem of irreversibility in physics is really many problems in one. Here we shall only attempt to outline questions that are still argued today by the experts, and indicate the kind of solution that is at least acceptable to many. As we said at the start of this book, one may argue that statistical mechanics, strictly speaking, has no concern with irreversible processes since these involve *non*-equilibrium macroscopic states, whereas statistical mechanics proper is a link between mechanics and equilibrium thermodynamics. Whether or not this outlook is really justified, it is in any case a somewhat narrow viewpoint; moreover, since in recent years much effort has in fact gone into trying to extend statistical thermodynamics to deal more adequately with nonequilibrium processes (e.g., the viscous flow of fluids, electrical resistivity, etc.), it seems worthwhile for us to be at least aware of some of the broad questions involved.

4.5.1 The Basic Problem in Outline

Consider a closed assembly, such as we have discussed frequently. We assume that the mechanical equations of motion governing the

* Compare again, e.g., Barron, 1957; see also Barron, 1956.

behavior of any and every element are either those of quantum mechanics (e.g., Schrödinger's equation), or else Newton's equations of motion leading directly to classical statistical mechanics which has been our main topic of discussion in this chapter. Now imagine that we do find our assembly initially in some macroscopic state which is well removed from that normally associated with thermodynamic equilibrium. For example, we might take the very simple model of an idealized paramagnetic solid of N elements, discussed in Chapter 1, and consider the extreme situation where all the elementary magnetic moments are oriented in the "up" state, and consequently the solid exhibits a saturation magnetic moment. That is, in this state, say at $t = 0$, the macroscopic magnetic moment $\mathfrak{M}$ is

$$\mathfrak{M}(0) = N\mathfrak{m}. \tag{165}$$

For the moment it need not concern us precisely *how* the assembly got into this state (either because we deliberately applied a strong enough external magnetic field or else because the assembly happened to be in this extremely rare state spontaneously). Be that as it may, what we now envisage is that any external magnetic field that *may* have been present is removed at $t = 0$, and the system then proceeds "on its own," so to speak.

General experience of physics tells us that the macroscopic magnetic moment $\mathfrak{M}(t)$ will then decay essentially towards a zero magnetic moment with some typical "relaxation time" τ. The simplest law likely to be followed by this decay is that

$$\mathfrak{M}(t) = \mathfrak{M}(0)e^{-t/\tau} \tag{166a}$$

(cf. Fig. 21*a*); or equivalently we may say that the magnetic moment will decay following the idealized "relaxation equation"

$$\frac{d\mathfrak{M}}{dt} = -\frac{\mathfrak{M}}{\tau}. \tag{166b}$$

Somewhat more generally, if the final equilibrium macroscopic state involves a magnetic moment $\mathfrak{M}_{eq}$ (rather than our particular assumption that $\mathfrak{M}_{eq} = 0$), then in the idealized case we might expect a decay law for the macroscopic magnetic moment

$$\frac{d\mathfrak{M}}{dt} = -\frac{\mathfrak{M} - \mathfrak{M}_{eq}}{\tau}. \tag{166c}$$

Now this type of equation is essentially irreversible in time t, and the

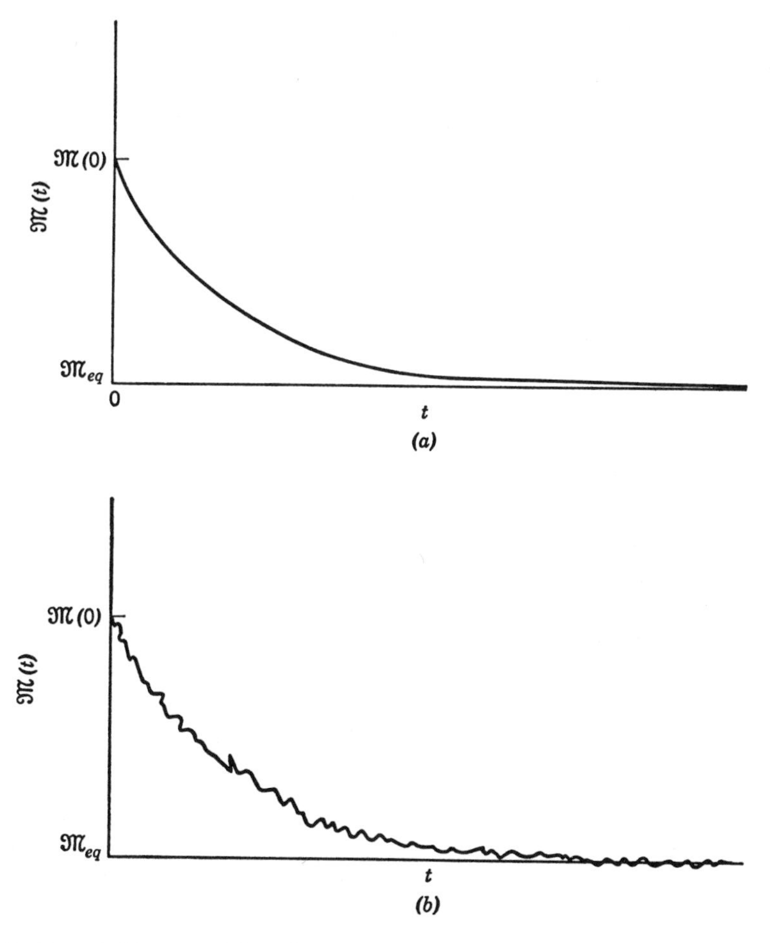

FIG. 21. To illustrate "decay" or "relaxation" of system towards equilibrium state.

(*a*) **Sketch** indicating idealized relaxation of some macroscopic parameter [say $\mathfrak{M}(t)$] towards thermodynamic equilibrium, say $\mathfrak{M} = \mathfrak{M}_{eq}$, following ideally the equation:

$$\mathfrak{M}(t) - \mathfrak{M}_{eq} = \{\mathfrak{M}(0) - \mathfrak{M}_{eq}\}e^{-t/\tau},$$

where τ is the "relaxation time."

(*b*) **Sketch** indicating relaxation of $\mathfrak{M}(t)$ with typical spontaneous fluctuations also present.

The interpretation of irreversible behavior outlined in the text requires us to envisage the initial state $\mathfrak{M}(0)$ as able to arise *in principle* from an extremely rare and large spontaneous fluctuation; thereafter ($t > 0$) however, the fluctuations will *almost certainly* be of relatively small magnitude as indicated, and are presumed only to become significant again in relation to $\mathfrak{M}(t) - \mathfrak{M}_{eq}$ when $\mathfrak{M}(t)$ is very close to $\mathfrak{M}_{eq}$.

essence of this remark can be expressed in different equivalent ways.* Physically, Eq. 166*a*, *b*, or *c* tells us that, if we start from some initial condition at $t = 0$, as time progresses in the accepted sense (t in these equations increasing positively towards ∞), the system changes progressively *in a perfectly monotonic manner* (in particular $\mathfrak{M} \rightarrow \mathfrak{M}_{eq}$), and moreover that, however far the time t proceeds, the system according to these equations would never "retrace its steps." Another way of expressing this irreversible behavior in time is to observe that mathematically the equations change their form fundamentally if we write $-t$ for t. In particular, the law $\mathfrak{M} \sim e^{-t/\tau}$ as t increases is obviously entirely different in character from a law $\mathfrak{M} \sim e^{+t/\tau}$ as t increases.

So far so good. But now, if we are also to believe that the whole isolated assembly can ultimately be described by mechanical equations of motion, we appear to meet a basic dilemma. Let us confine ourselves in all that follows to the problem of classical Newtonian mechanics, and similarly to classical statistical mechanics. Classical equations of motion are ultimately based on "elementary" Newtonian equations of the form

$$\frac{d^2x}{dt^2} = F(x, y), \tag{167}$$

where x is some displacement-like coordinate, and y stands for (possibly) many other displacement-like coordinates. The vital feature is now that Eq. 167 does *not* alter its fundamental form when we replace t by $-t$.† That is to say, *mechanical* equations of motion of them-

* We shall restrict the rest of our discussion to assemblies assumed to obey classical mechanics. For such assemblies various ways of expressing irreversibility in time are indeed all equivalent. If we turn to quantum mechanics, then the concensus of opinion is probably: that first there is nothing *inherently* irreversible about quantum mechanics (and consequently that one's broad conclusions here will be the same as for classical mechanical systems), but secondly that it is more difficult in quantum mechanics to express uniquely what one means by a reversible system. In other words, and very roughly speaking, reversibility in time means in the end only one thing in classical mechanics, but it is probably a more ambiguous concept in quantum mechanics (cf. also second footnote to p. 10).

Perhaps we should say that we are also excluding any possible relativistic effects in this sketchy discussion.

† The important feature is that such time derivatives as occur are always of *even* order. This remains true for more complex mechanical differential equations such as that for vibration in a three-dimensional medium

$$\frac{\partial^2 u}{\partial x^2} + \frac{\partial^2 u}{\partial y^2} + \frac{\partial^2 u}{\partial z^2} = \frac{1}{c^2}\frac{\partial^2 u}{\partial t^2}.$$

This feature is in direct contrast to the well-known *phenomenological* equation

selves are fundamentally "reversible" in time t. To take a basic case, if one believes (as one does) that Newton's mechanics will describe extraordinarily well the motion of an isolated planet about the sun, the mechanics will do equally well whether the planet goes around the sun to eternity in a clockwise fashion, or if it had "chosen" instead to go around in an anticlockwise direction.* When discussing specifically the concept of entropy, both Eddington and Schrödinger have used the expression "the arrow of time," and the general dilemma of irreversibility in physics may be expressed by saying that mechanics *itself* does not appear to carry any "arrow of time." How then can an isolated assembly of elements (atoms, molecules, etc.) carry out an irreversible process, such as that described by Eqs. 166*a*, *b*, or *c*, when our whole foundation of statistical mechanics rests on the assumption that each element obeys mechanical equations of motion, and that no further vital assumptions are really necessary in order to arrive at the macroscopic results of statistical mechanics? Indeed the very reversibility of mechanics is essentially what we invoked in setting up our statistical mechanics, because our basic assumption that all mechanical states were "*a priori* equally probable" rests, as Planck in effect pointed out, on the fact that mechanics itself knows no difference between time going forward or backwards.

The general problem of the "reversibility-irreversibility paradox" was very sensitively appreciated by Boltzmann himself, and is therefore far from a new question (see, e.g., the excellent review by Chandrasekhar (1943), particularly the historical survey of irreversibility problems on p. 54 et seq. of that review). The problem presents itself in many different forms, all in the end related to this general discussion; thus, e.g., how one is to calculate quantitatively such *irreversible* prop-

---

for diffusion

$$\frac{\partial f}{\partial t} = D\frac{\partial^2 f}{\partial x^2}$$

(in one dimension for convenience), and the heat conduction equation (again in one dimension):

$$C\frac{\partial T}{\partial t} = \kappa\frac{\partial^2 T}{\partial x^2}.$$

Both these latter differential equations involve *first-order* time derivatives, and indeed correspond to physically irreversible processes.

* Of course the "awkward" reader may well ask *who* decides what is to be called "clockwise," and what is to be called "anticlockwise," when we are dealing with an isolated planet around an isolated sun. The point is well taken, and is perhaps just another aspect of the "inherent reversibility" of an isolated mechanical system.

erties as fluid viscosity, frictional constants, or turbulent behavior, using atomic parameters and *mechanical* equations as one's basic apparatus. Let us try to outline the philosophy behind a solution to the apparent paradox involved (cf. again Chandrasekhar, 1943), a solution which would be acceptable to many, though not to all.*

We would first say that Eq. 166*a*, *b*, or *c* (and see Fig. 21*a*) does not describe *exactly* the subsequent course of events. We argue rather that the system decays following this equation very closely until the typical "spontaneous fluctuations" of the assembly become dominant† (see now Fig. 21*b*). To complete the picture we assume that it does not really matter whether the initial state at $t = 0$ actually presented itself "by chance" (extremely rarely!—and cf. Section 1.4) as part of its over-all behavior which is reversible if observed over *sufficiently long* time intervals, or whether in fact we "prepared" the system artificially.‡ Thus we may regard the proposed initial state at $t = 0$ as an extremely rare "spontaneous fluctuation" of the system, and therefore, because of the extreme rarity of such a state in nature, the system will *appear* to move irreversibly within any time interval of normal human experience towards the more common so-called equilibrium states. That is, we need never expect to see the system "go back" by itself to the original state, although fundamentally we argue that the possibility exists *in principle*, because we maintain that the behavior of the assembly is reversible over *sufficiently long time intervals*. In more technical language, we are saying that over sufficiently long time intervals the behavior of the closed assembly would ultimately be found to be cyclic and hence reversible in time; however, the expected time of recurrence (a so-called Poincaré cycle) of any significant deviation from the "most probable" states of the assembly (i.e., macroscopic states of thermodynamic equilibrium) will in general be enormously long (cf. again, e.g., Chandrasekhar, 1943). So, to repeat, from this viewpoint the behavior of the closed assembly is, in the last analysis, truly reversible

* At the risk of being tedious we repeat that the problem still excites much interest today, and there is still some considerable clash of opinion on how the transition from basic reversibility to macroscopic irreversibility should best be made in analysis—and indeed there is even still argument today on where exactly the transition was made in an analysis, even when it has been carried out! (cf., e.g., Brussells Conference, 1956).

† For simplicity here we are assuming that $\mathfrak{M}_{eq} = 0$.

‡ This assumption boils down to saying that it is sufficient to know the *present* state of the assembly (*without* knowing its previous "history") in order to discuss adequately in statistical mechanics its future behavior. In technical terms we are assuming what is called "Markovian behavior."

Although the assumption is most appealing, the difficulty is to satisfy oneself fully that it is really warranted.

in time, but within human experience (or indeed human history) will *appear* to behave irreversibly when starting from any "non-equilibrium" macroscopic state, whether occurring "by chance" or deliberately prepared.

4.5.2 Fluctuations and the "Ergodic Theorem"

With this viewpoint, we may also draw the moral that the "spontaneous fluctuations" ("Brownian Movement" or "thermal noise") of thermodynamic systems actually offer rather direct evidence that the various mechanical states (Newtonian or quantum mechanical) are indeed being "explored" by the assembly without fear or favor and in a basically quite reversible manner. This essentially is the physical content of the so-called Ergodic Theorem, which we mentioned previously in Section 1.2.4. Thus it is argued that, in principle, *any* permissible macroscopic condition can and will occur and recur as time goes by (if we wait long enough!), but if the macroscopic condition corresponds to "microscopic" configurations of very low statistical weight, then the time of recurrence (Poincaré cycle) will be enormously long, and in fact *only* by preparing a system artificially shall we ever be likely to encounter this macroscopic state at all.

The Brownian Movement Approximation.* The essentials of the situation are illustrated rather well by the so-called "Brownian Movement Approximation." We consider now some isolated assembly such as a container of liquid at temperature T. In the liquid we immerse an observable particle of matter (the "Brownian" particle), which on the one hand is small enough to be sensitive to variations in the molecular collisions from the surrounding liquid, but on the other hand is large enough to be directly observable in its movement and to be describable adequately by classical coordinates. If we write as the equation of motion for such a particle,

$$\frac{dP}{dt} = \mathfrak{F}(t), \tag{168a}$$

* The name refers to the English biologist, Robert Brown, who in 1827 observed the spontaneous "Brownian Movement" of tiny particles of pollen dust in water when examining the dust through a microscope. Brown himself believed at first from his observations of this behavior with various types of dust that this spontaneous and incessant movement was associated with some fundamental form of life. It was Einstein who established theoretically, with adequate certainty, that the Brownian Movement arose fundamentally from the bombardment of the particles by the surrounding fluid molecules (for a fuller discussion of the historical origins and development of the analysis of Brownian Movement, and of other forms of noise, see, e.g., MacDonald, 1962).

then Langevin proposed as a description of the behavior of such a particle in statistical equilibrium with the surrounding liquid that we should write

$$\frac{dP}{dt} = -\frac{P}{\tau} + F(t). \tag{168b}$$

Equation 168*a* would be essentially a mechanical, and basically reversible, equation of motion for the momentum P of the Brownian particle taking into account in $\mathfrak{F}(t)$, strictly speaking, all the appropriate individual interactions (more loosely, "collisions") with the surrounding liquid molecules. Langevin's equation 168*b* then separates the overall force $\mathfrak{F}(t)$ into two parts: the "macroscopic" or "average" force on the particle, presumed to be ideally of the form $-P/\tau$ (an idealized "viscous" force), and the remaining very rapidly fluctuating, and more or less random, part of the force acting on the particle. If Eq. 168*b* indeed derives from Eq. 168*a* then, since the term $-P/\tau$ *by itself* would yield a macroscopically irreversible behavior, then *so also* must the fluctuating term $F(t)$ have some irreversible character, so that the *two terms together* will add up to give the original equation 168*a*, which is presumed to be basically reversible. If now we regard the Brownian particle itself as a system of interest which we are observing, then normally speaking both terms on the right-hand side of Eq. 168*b* are of importance so that neither can be neglected, and indeed we can say that the particle will "fluctuate" close to the state $P = 0$ in a quite reversible manner. If, however, by rare chance, or because we deliberately give the particle a shove, P becomes rather large, then for the next little while the effect of the term $-P/\tau$ in Eq. 168*b* will almost certainly be much greater than that of the residual "fluctuating" term $F(t)$. Thus if we neglect $F(t)$ entirely for the present, we have simply

$$\frac{dP}{dt} = -\frac{P}{\tau}, \tag{168c}$$

which is now the familiar "relaxation equation" (cf. Eq. 166*b*) and apparently irreversible in time. The point to be made here is that we only arrive at an apparently irreversible decay equation by neglecting the fluctuations entirely, whereas in fact the required over-all symmetry in time (i.e., over-all reversibility) would actually be made up in Langevin's equation 168*b* because there would always be an equal number of (very rare) occasions—if the isolated assembly is left strictly to itself—when the fluctuating term $F(t)$ would become the dominant term in that equation. These occasions would occur when a large (and very rare) fluctuation in P is "spontaneously" built up for the Brownian particle. Thus the moral again would be that what we call the spontaneous fluctuations of systems are really quite vital if we are to understand how apparently irreversible behavior comes about (cf. also MacDonald, 1961, for some further remarks).

A further and final point that we can derive from the approximation of Langevin's equation 168*b* is to see from this point of view how the very equilibrium distribution is maintained physically, e.g., the Maxwell-Boltzmann distribution or more generally the so-called canonical distribution function for classical systems. The familiar Gaussian distribution function of momenta, symmetrical about zero, can be thought of for any given element as being perpetuated dynamically in a rather direct way. If an element happens to have its momentum close to zero, then the fluctuating force $F(t)$ in Langevin's equation will tend to jog its momentum further away from zero. On the other hand, as soon as its momentum has become at all large, the "viscous" part of the force $-P/\tau$ will tend to drag the momentum back towards zero. The dynamic balance between these two "opposing" effects can be thought of as maintaining the normal equilibrium distribution. (And this argument can be made quite quantitative, leading indeed to the canonical distribution.)

However, if we disturb "from outside" this generally balanced situation by setting up deliberately a nonequilibrium state, or else consciously wait long enough for some very rare configuration to occur, then the normal balance of these two terms in the Langevin equation is upset so that the "viscous" term $(-P/\tau)$ dominates the situation for the time being, and consequently appears explicitly in the equation governing the subsequent approach to equilibrium.

The Distribution Function in Nonequilibrium Situations. The basic job of extending statistical mechanics to deal with irreversible processes is that of deriving with some certainty distribution functions valid for nonequilibrium situations. In the "Brownian Movement approximation" where the system of interest is relatively large compared with the immediate environment, this problem is largely solved by the so-called *Fokker-Planck equation.** This differential equation for the distribution function expresses analytically the two

* At least this is true for linear systems (see, e.g., MacDonald, 1962). For nonlinear systems (see Alkemade, van Kampen, and MacDonald, 1963) one has to go further, and a popular outlook today is that the so-called Master Equation is the most promising general starting point for the analysis of irreversible processes; it can be shown that the Fokker-Planck equation itself represents the first terms of a systematic expansion of the Master Equation (cf. again Alkemade et al., *loc. cit.*).

opposing "forces" at work, namely the fluctuations and the viscosity, and the physics of the Fokker-Planck equation for the distribution function is identical with that behind Langevin's equation.

For a Brownian particle, or some similar semimacroscopic system, the Fokker-Planck equation shows, for example, very adequately how the system will return from arbitrary initial conditions to the final canonical equilibrium distribution, and indeed the final equilibrium predicted by the Fokker-Planck equation agrees precisely with what we should derive directly from (equilibrium) statistical mechanics.

However, when we come to deal with the distribution function for more "fundamental" elements such as molecules, atoms, electrons, etc., and we wish to discuss *nonequilibrium* problems, there is still considerable argument today as to how valid are the various approximations involved; there is probably still much exciting work to be done in the field.

APPENDIX I

BASIC EXPRESSIONS FOR "LOCALIZABLE" ELEMENTS

1 CALCULATION OF Ω

1.1 Statement of Problem

We can state our problem in two equivalent ways:

(1) (The more usual mode of expression). In how many distinguishable ways can we arrange N objects in N different locations in space (e.g., on points on a line) if n_1 of these objects are of one kind (and indistinguishable from one another), and the remainder ($n_2 = N - n_1$) are of some other kind, indistinguishable from one another?

More generally we consider the problem with n_1 objects of one kind indistinguishable from one another, n_2 of a second kind indistinguishable from one another, n_3 of a third kind . . . , such that

$$n_1 + n_2 + n_3 + \cdots = N.$$

(2) Given N "sites" or locations in space (and this need not necessarily be "real" space), in how many different ways can we "label" n_1 of these sites with one kind of label, (say 1), and the remainder of the sites with another kind of label (say 2)?

Let us use the first statement of the problem for the analysis, although I suggest that the second statement is actually a better physical picture to bear in mind for statistical mechanics.

1.2 Analysis

If the N objects were *all* different from one another, we could first pick out any one of the N objects and place it on the first point in space, next fill the second spot with any one of the remaining $N - 1$ objects, and so on. Thus the total number of possible distinguishable arrangements in this case would be $N!$.

Consider now dividing these N objects into two groups, n_1 and n_2 $(= N - n_1)$ in number, and let us set out first *any* single arrangement of the n_2 objects. Given this particular arrangement of the n_2 objects we can then arrange the remaining n_1 objects in $n_1!$ ways. If, however, these n_1 objects are *indistinguishable* among themselves, we can only arrange them in one way for any given distribution of the n_2 distinguishable objects. That is, the total number of distinguishable arrangements will thus be reduced by $n_1!$ if n_1 of the N objects are indistinguishable; i.e., if n_1 of the N objects are identical, the total number of distinguishable configurations will be $N!/n_1!$. If moreover the subgroup of n_2 objects $(n_2 = N - n_1)$ are *also* indistinguishable among themselves, evidently the total number of distinguishable configurations Ω will then be given by

$$\Omega = \frac{N!}{n_1!n_2!} = \frac{N!}{n_1!(N - n_1)!}. \tag{169}$$

More generally, therefore, if n_1 of the objects are of one kind which are indistinguishable from one another, n_2 are of another kind indistinguishable from one another, and so on, the total number of distinguishable arrangements will be given by

$$\Omega = \frac{N!}{n_1!n_2! \cdots n_i! \cdots}. \tag{170}$$

1.3 Introduction of Degeneracy

We return to our N locations in space with N distinguishable objects, but moreover we assume now that each of these distinguishable objects can present g different "faces." (For example, we might have N differently colored conventional dice, and thus $g = 6$, corresponding to the six different faces of a particular die.) We can now fill the first location with any one of the N objects, and can then "expose" any one of the g faces; i.e., we can fill the first place in any one of Ng ways. The second place can then be filled with any one of the remaining $N - 1$ objects, and again we can choose any one of the g faces of that object, and so on. Thus the total number of configurations will now be

$$\Omega = N!g^N. \tag{171}$$

If now the objects remain all distinguishable from one another, but

n_1 have g_1 faces, n_2 have g_2 faces, and so on, then Eq. 171 is obviously modified to read

$$\Omega = N!g_1^{n_1}g_2^{n_2} \cdots g_i^{n_i} \cdots . \tag{172}$$

Finally, if the group of n_1 objects are indistinguishable among themselves, the group of n_2 objects indistinguishable in *that* group, and so on, we must once again divide by $n_1!n_2! \ldots$ as in arriving at Eq. 170, so that we have ultimately:

$$\Omega = \frac{N!g_1^{n_1}g_2^{n_2} \cdots g_i^{n_i} \cdots}{n_1!n_2! \cdots n_i! \cdots}. \tag{173}$$

2 MODERATE DEVIATIONS FROM MOST PROBABLE STATE

We consider the simple "heads and tails" model discussed in the text, with N localizable elements (e.g., pennies) in all. (Individual "heads" or "tails" are equally probable; or in atomic terms the two individual atomic states have identical energies.) The most probable state of the whole assembly is then of course that with equal numbers ($N/2$) of "heads" and "tails," and the number of distinguishable configurations corresponding to this state is $\Omega_{\max} = N! \Big/ \frac{N}{2}!\frac{N}{2}!$.
Consider now a deviation from this most probable state such that the excess of "heads" over "tails" is $2n$. Thus the number of configurations, say $\tilde{\omega}$, corresponding to this particular state of the assembly, is

$$\tilde{\omega} = \frac{N!}{\left(\frac{N}{2} + n\right)!\left(\frac{N}{2} - n\right)!} \tag{174a}$$

For large values of N and $n \ll N$ (i.e., modest deviations from the "most probable" state), Eq. 174*a* is excellently approximated by

$$\tilde{\omega} = 2^N \left(\frac{2}{\pi N}\right)^{1/2} e^{-2n^2/N}. \tag{174b*}$$

* For the transition from Eq. 174*a* to 174*b* we require Stirling's approximation for factorials. Stirling's formula may be written

$$\ln N! = N \ln N - N + \ln (2\pi N)^{1/2} + \text{terms of order } 1/N. \tag{175a}$$

In the present situation we require the first three terms on the right-hand side of Stirling's formula. For the remainder of our work, however, it suffices to use the lower order of approximation

$$\ln N! \approx N \ln N - N \tag{175b}$$

Moreover since the overwhelming majority of configurations are in fact found for $n \ll N$ we shall assume that Eq. 174*b* will suffice adequately in this discussion for all values of n.

We now wish to know the number of configurations in all, say ω, which provide a relative excess of "heads" over "tails" ($2n/N$) such that $2n/N \geq 10^{-6}$; on our simplest paramagnetic salt model this would correspond to a spontaneous magnetic moment $\geq 10^{-6}$ of the *saturation* moment. Thus

$$\omega \approx 2^N \left(\frac{2}{\pi N}\right)^{1/2} \int_{\frac{2n}{N}=10^{-6}}^{\frac{2n}{N}=+\infty} e^{-2n^2/N}\, dn; \tag{176}$$

this integral will be an excellent approximation for ω since the (actual) unit increments in n will be extremely small in comparison with N. The upper limit of the integral is written as infinity for convenience since the integrand at the true upper limit will certainly have become entirely negligible in comparison with its value at the *lower* limit. So

$$\omega \approx 2^N \left(\frac{1}{\sqrt{\pi}}\right) \int_{10^{-6}\sqrt{N/2}}^{\infty} e^{-y^2}\, dy;$$

with $N \approx 10^{16}$ (cf. section 1.4), this gives

$$\omega \approx \frac{2^N}{\pi^{1/2}} \frac{e^{-10^4}}{2 \cdot 10^2}, \quad \text{i.e., Eq. 15}a. \tag{177}$$

[We have used the result that

$$\int_z^{\infty} e^{-t^2}\, dt \approx \frac{e^{-z^2}}{2z}\left(1 - \frac{1}{2z^2} + \cdots\right).]$$

But we know already that the *total* number of possible configurations is $\Omega = 2^N$, and consequently the relative probability P for observing spontaneously the proposed deviation of the state of the assembly from its "most probable" state is

$$P = \frac{\omega}{\Omega} \approx \frac{e^{-10^4}}{2\sqrt{\pi} \cdot 10^2} \approx \frac{e^{-10^4}}{3 \cdot 10^2}, \tag{178}$$

as in Eq. 15*b*.

APPENDIX II
ASSEMBLY OF LOCALIZED ELEMENTS

We consider an assembly of N localized elements, or in that sense "distinguishable" particles, and each of these particles may occupy any one of a number of possible elementary states which, for the present, we shall assume are all nondegenerate (i.e., each elementary state carries a different particle energy). Let things be so arranged that n_1 of the particles are in state 1 of energy ϵ_1, the number in state 2 is n_2, etc. Then the number of distinguishable ways (complexions), say $\tilde{\Omega}$, for this particular distribution to occur is

$$\tilde{\Omega} = \frac{N!}{n_1!n_2! \cdots n_i! \cdots}, \tag{179}$$

(i.e., Eq. 170 of Appendix I). We can now vary the particular numbers n_1, n_2, etc., in any way we please *so long as we satisfy*

$$\sum_i n_i = N, \tag{180}$$

and

$$\sum_i n_i\epsilon_i = E, \tag{181}$$

where N is the total number of particles in the assembly and E is the total energy, both assumed constant. The sum of all values of $\tilde{\Omega}$, when we vary n_1, n_2, etc., in this way, will then yield the *total* number Ω of permissible, distinguishable configurations of the assembly.

We then argue (cf. Section 1.4, Fig. 3, and Table 1) that it will be sufficient to find the values of n_1, n_2, etc., which would yield a *maximum* value for $\tilde{\Omega}$, say $\Omega_{\max}$, in Eq. 179 (subject to the conditions of Eqs. 180 and 181) in order to give us an adequate estimate for the desired *total* number of permissible configurations Ω. More properly (cf. Table 1) it is $\ln \Omega_{max}$ which gives an entirely adequate estimate of $\ln \Omega$ as required for the entropy S.

Factorials are awkward to deal with analytically, and so long as the numbers involved are sufficiently large (as is generally true in statistical mechanics), we may use Stirling's approximation in the form

$$\boxed{\ln n! \approx n \ln n - n}, \tag{182}$$

(cf. footnote to Eq. 174*b*, Appendix I). That is, from Eq. 179

$$\ln \tilde{\Omega} = N \ln N - N - \sum_i (n_i \ln n_i - n_i). \tag{183}$$

We now seek a maximum of the expression in Eq. 183 subject to the conditions of Eqs. 180 and 181 (i.e., we seek $\ln \Omega_{max}$).

Let us first consider the very simple case of the "heads, tails" problem, which we used as a first approximate model for a simple paramagnetic solid. In this very simple case we have to consider only the restrictive condition of Eq. 180, i.e.,

$$n_1 + n_2 = N, \tag{184}$$

and we know already that the *exact* answer for the *total* number of configurations Ω is

$$\Omega = 2^N, \quad \text{i.e., } \ln \Omega = N \ln 2. \tag{185}$$

Now let us seek $\ln \Omega_{max}$. From Eqs. 183 and 184 we have

$$\ln \tilde{\Omega} = N \ln N - n_1 \ln n_1 - (N - n_1) \ln (N - n_1); \tag{186}$$

therefore

$$\frac{d \ln \tilde{\Omega}}{dn_1} = -1 - \ln n_1 + 1 + \ln (N - n_1),$$

which vanishes to yield a maximum for $\tilde{\Omega} = \Omega_{max}$, when

$$n_1 = N - n_1, \quad \text{i.e., } n_1 = \frac{N}{2}. \tag{187}$$

i.e., Ω_{max} occurs for $n_1 = n_2 = N/2$, a very familiar result, and then from Eq. 186 we have

$$\ln \Omega_{max} = N \ln 2. \tag{188}$$

Thus in this simple case we find that (within our use of Stirling's approximation) $\ln \Omega_{max}$ is in fact *indistinguishable* from $\ln \Omega$ (Eq. 185); this justifies in a welcome manner the use of $\ln \Omega_{max}$ in place of $\ln \Omega$.

We return now to the more general situation of Eq. 183 with the two restrictive conditions of Eqs. 180 and 181. It proves easiest then to include these conditions when seeking the maximum of $\ln \tilde{\Omega}$ by using so-called Lagrange undetermined multipliers. What this boils down to is that in effect we first incorporate the two restrictive conditions in the original expression for $\ln \tilde{\Omega}$, and then seek straightforwardly an over-all maximum. So long as we *satisfy* Eq. 180 we have

$$\sum_i n_i - N = 0,$$

or more generally

$$\alpha\left(\sum_i n_i - N\right) = 0,$$

where α is at this stage quite arbitrary. Similarly, if we satisfy Eq. 181, we can write

$$\beta\left(\sum_i n_i\epsilon_i - E\right) = 0,$$

where β here is also arbitrary.

Thus *if the restrictive conditions are satisfied*, we may write

$$\ln \tilde{\Omega} = N \ln N - N - \sum_i (n_i \ln n_i - n_i) + \alpha\left(\sum_i n_i - N\right) + \beta\left(\sum_i n_i\epsilon_i - E\right). \quad (189)$$

All we have to do (and this procedure can be readily justified in algebraic detail) is to seek directly a maximum of this latter expression, treating now the variables n_i as *free* of restriction, i.e., as independent of one another, and of course treating N and E as constants. For the maximum of $\ln \tilde{\Omega}$, as given by Eq. 189, we must then simply satisfy

$$\frac{\partial \ln \tilde{\Omega}}{\partial n_i} = 0, \qquad \textbf{for each and every } \mathbf{n_i},$$

giving

$$\ln n_i = \alpha + \beta\epsilon_i. \quad (189a)$$

That is,

$$\boxed{n_i = e^{\alpha+\beta\epsilon_i}}, \qquad \textbf{for each and every } \mathbf{n_i}. \quad (189b)$$

In this very fundamental expression for the internal distribution in an assembly of localized elements (or "distinguishable" elements), we can readily eliminate α without inquiring about its significance. (But we should note that α has a very important role to play in *non-localizable*, or "gaslike," assemblies which we considered in Chapter 3; see also Appendix III or IV.) We have $\sum_i n_i = N$, and hence

$$N = e^{\alpha} \sum_i e^{\beta \epsilon_i},$$

or from Eq. 189*b*

$$\boxed{n_i = N \frac{e^{\beta \epsilon_i}}{\sum_i e^{\beta \epsilon_i}} = \frac{N}{Z} e^{\beta \epsilon_i}}, \qquad (190)$$

where α no longer appears, and where by definition Z is the "partition function per element," i.e., $Z = \sum_i e^{\beta \epsilon_i}$ for an assembly with non-degenerate energy levels.

Returning to Eq. 183 for $\ln \tilde{\Omega}$ and using Eq. 190 for the "most probable" value of n_i to give $\ln \Omega_{\max}$, we find

$$\ln \Omega_{\max} = N \ln Z - \beta \sum_i n_i \epsilon_i; \qquad (191a)$$

but $\sum_i n_i \epsilon_i = E$, hence

$$\ln \Omega_{\max} = N \ln Z - \beta E. \qquad (191b)$$

Now $S = k \ln \Omega$, and using $\ln \Omega_{\max}$ as an entirely adequate approximation for $\ln \Omega$, we have

$$S = Nk \ln Z - \beta k E, \qquad (192a)$$

or for a mole of the substance

$$S = R \ln Z - \beta k E, \qquad (192b)$$

where E is then the internal energy per mole. Finally, substituting $\beta = -1/kT$, we have for the molar entropy

$$S = R \ln Z + \frac{E}{T}, \qquad (192c)$$

which is just Eq. 17.

COMMENTS

(1) Identification and Significance of β

We can make the identification of β by showing first analytically, starting from Eq. 192*a*, that

$$\left(\frac{\partial S}{\partial E}\right)_{N,V} = -k\beta, \tag{193}$$

and then secondly appealing to thermodynamics which tells us that

$$\left(\frac{\partial S}{\partial E}\right) = \frac{1}{T}, \tag{194}$$

i.e., $\beta = -1/kT$, as assumed above.

The direct relationship of β with temperature is of course no accident. The parameter β is introduced when we incorporate our restrictive condition on the total energy E. The importance of this condition on the energy is not merely that it says we are dealing ideally with an isolated assembly (and hence that the over-all energy is fixed at some value E) but, and very importantly, that the various elements in the assembly are quite *free* to exchange energy with one another, subject *only* to the requirement that the total energy remains constant. It is precisely here that the physical concept of an assembly in thermal equilibrium is "injected" mathematically into our analysis. Imagine that in our assembly we had some barrier dividing it into two parts, a and b, such that energy could *not* be exchanged between a and b. Then physically this would mean that the two parts could remain indefinitely at different temperatures T_a and T_b; at the same time, denoting the particles in a in some state i by $n_{a,i}$ and those in b in some state j by $n_{b,j}$, we should now have to include as restrictive conditions

$$\sum_i n_{a,i}\epsilon_i = E_a, \quad \text{and} \quad \sum_j n_{b,j}\epsilon_j = E_b \tag{195a}$$

(as well as)

$$\sum_i n_{a,i} = N_a, \quad \text{and} \quad \sum_j n_{b,j} = N_b. \tag{195b}$$

Then to take account of the pair of restrictive conditions on energy, Eq. 195*a*, we would have to introduce mathematically *two* β's, β_a, and β_b, directly corresponding to the physical concept of the two temperatures T_a and T_b. In other words, the pair of restrictive conditions on energy express not merely that the two parts of the assembly are thermally insulated from one another, but, and very importantly, that *within* each part of the assembly, thermal equilibrium, or in effect unrestricted energy exchange, is possible.

(2) Independent Thermodynamic Variables and Types of Ensembles

The formula $S = Nk \ln Z - \beta k E$ (Eq. 192*a*), strictly speaking, purports to have expressed the entropy S as a function of E, V, and N. Indeed in this equation S is obviously a function of N and E, and moreover the elementary energy levels ϵ_i occurring in Z will in general depend to some degree on V, but be governed in detail by the particular model we are dealing with. This still leaves the parameter β undetermined from this point of view. *In principle,* knowing again the details of the particular model involved, we might express β also as a function of E, N, and V (the latter through some knowledge of the energy levels ϵ_i), but this would be a very complex operation except for the simplest models. For an assembly of similar harmonic oscillators of frequency ν, one can in fact write

$$S = Nk \ln\left(1 + \frac{E}{Nh\nu}\right) + \frac{E}{h\nu} k \ln\left(1 + \frac{Nh\nu}{E}\right), \tag{196}$$

where β does not appear, and where E is the energy measured from a zero level such that $E = 0$ at $T = 0$. (In other words, in each oscillator the energy is measured from the quantum ground-state.) Thus in this particularly simple case we have in fact expressed S as a function of E, N, and V (assuming that ν is a function of V, as we should expect).

We repeat then that *in principle* we can arrive at an expression for the entropy S in terms of E, N, and V, and we can then, if we wish, *deduce* the temperature T of our statistical assembly, using the relation $\partial S/\partial E = 1/T$. However, it is far more natural and convenient in physical science to regard the temperature T *as given,** and then to *deduce* the energy E, etc.; and moreover for any macroscopic assembly the relationship is unique. That is to say, given the temperature (and N and V), we can regard the energy E of the assembly as being

* Personally I would argue that this stems basically from the fact that the human being is directly sensitive to temperature in some degree or other, just as he is directly sensitive to light and darkness. One job of science is to translate physiological sensations into precise, and objective, definitions and operations such as "hot" and "cold," "heavy" and "light," but it certainly seems most natural that we try to retain (after attaining precision and objectivity) as our "independent variables" essentially those that we are aware of directly as human beings.

fully determined, equally validly with saying that the temperature T is determined when we know E, N, and V.*

By the time we arrive at the expression for the Helmholtz free energy per mole

$$F = -RT \ln Z \tag{197}$$

(which is Eq. 20), we have really completed the transition from E, V, and N as independent variables to T, V, and N. Equation 192*c* for S is a sort of hybrid expression, since *both* the energy E and the temperature T appear explicitly, but in Eq. 197 for F the transformation to T as independent variable is now complete.

If we attack statistical mechanics by starting from an assembly at constant E, V, and N (as we have done) then, strictly speaking, we are using in technical language a "micro-canonical ensemble." It is also possible to approach more immediately an expression like Eq. 197 by considering our particular assembly, *not* as being isolated (at strictly constant E), but rather in thermal contact with a large number of *other* similar assemblies forming in effect a "heat bath." This heat bath now determines primarily the *temperature*, T, of any particular assembly. This approach to statistical mechanics would mean that, technically speaking, we were using a so-called "canonical ensemble." The unique relationship of E with T for macroscopic systems, which we have already mentioned, ensures that the end-results are identical using either approach.

The "Grand Canonical Ensemble." For the sake of completeness let us mention a further point, but let it not worry the reader! In each of the two approaches to statistical mechanics just mentioned, we are dealing with assemblies that are *closed* as regards number of elements or particles (i.e., N is to be constant in both cases). In the micro-canonical ensemble, the system is closed *and* insulated (i.e., energy may not be exchanged with the "outside world"), whereas in the canonical ensemble the systems are closed but in thermal contact with the outside world (i.e., energy may be freely exchanged). It is possible, if we wish, to go even further and make a *third* approach by allowing each of the individual assemblies now to be "open" to one another, as well as in thermal contact with one another. In other

* The essence of the matter is that we assume, strictly speaking, in thermodynamics that the over-all systems we study are large enough for fluctuations to be neglected. If we have a strictly isolated system, then by definition the total energy E is *strictly* constant. If on the other hand it is in contact with some very large thermal reservoir determining the temperature T, then the total energy of the system we are studying will fluctuate "spontaneously" to some extent; but essentially in equilibrium statistical mechanics we are assuming that such fluctuations are quite negligible.

words, not only may the individual assemblies freely exchange energy, but they may also freely exchange particles or elements with one another. To adopt such an approach to statistical mechanics is to use what is called technically a "grand canonical ensemble." It means in effect that we also introduce into our partition function *from the beginning* the chemical potentials (which we discuss in Chapter 3; see also Appendices III and IV) of the individual assemblies; this partition function is then known in the jargon as the "grand partition function."

To summarize,

(*a*) If we use the "micro-canonical ensemble" (as we have done basically here), we evaluate our thermodynamic properties strictly speaking from *purely* mechanical quantities, and our basic bridge is the equation

$$S = k \ln \Omega. \tag{198}$$

(*b*) If we use the "canonical ensemble," we are recognizing from the start the concept of absolute temperature T as well as purely mechanical properties, and our bridge is then between F and the partition function Z; in particular for an assembly of N localized elements

$$F = -NkT \ln Z. \tag{199}$$

(*c*) In the "grand canonical ensemble" we introduce from the start the concepts of *both* temperature T *and* chemical potential. We shall not attempt here to discuss further this approach to statistical mechanics.

(3) Inclusion of Degeneracy

To include explicitly degeneracies g_i, we replace Eq. 179 with

$$\tilde{\Omega} = \frac{N! g_i^{n_1} g_2^{n_2} \cdots g_i^{n_i} \cdots}{n_1! n_2! \cdots n_i! \cdots} \quad \text{(cf. Eq. 173, Appendix I)}, \tag{179a}$$

$$\equiv N! \prod_i \frac{g_i^{n_i}}{n_i!}$$

and the analysis proceeds precisely as before, leading to

$$\ln n_i - \ln g_i = \alpha + \beta\epsilon_i, \quad \text{(in place of Eq. 189}a\text{)}, \tag{200a}$$

i.e.,

$$\boxed{n_i = g_i e^{\alpha + \beta\epsilon_i}}, \quad \text{(in place of Eq. 189}b\text{)}. \tag{200b}$$

The expressions in Section 1.5.2, such as Eq. 24*a*, follow directly.

APPENDIX III
BOSE-EINSTEIN STATISTICS

1 ANALYSIS

1.1 Number of Configurations

We have ω_1 particle states, and wish to know in how many different ways these may be occupied by n_1 identical particles, *there being no restriction* on how many particles may occupy any given particle state.

The complete freedom from restriction on the occupancy of any particle state allows one to use a rather direct method of counting for this particular problem, although it can be approached in another way (see Appendix V). Consider the following sketch for the case of $\omega_1 = 6$ and $n_1 = 11$:

$$. \; . \;|\; . \;|\;|\; . \; . \; . \; . \;|\; . \;|\; . \; . \; .$$

This would signify a distribution where there are two particles in the first state, one particle in the second, none in the third, four in the fourth, one in the fifth, and three particles in the sixth state. Notice that there are as many dots (.) as particles altogether, and one less bar (|) than the number of states (five bars for six states). More generally with n_1 dots and $\omega_1 - 1$ bars we can represent in this way every possible arrangement of n_1 identical particles in the ω_1 states by writing down (as in the sketch) these symbols (dots and bars) in any order we please. There are $n_1 + \omega_1 - 1$ symbols altogether, of which n_1 are of one type (dots), indistinguishable from one another, and $\omega_1 - 1$ of another type (bars) also indistinguishable from one another, and we wish to know the total number of distinguishable ways, Ω_1, of arranging these symbols.

The problem is now identical in form to that treated in Appendix I, so we can write immediately

$$\Omega_1 = \frac{(n_1 + \omega_1 - 1)!}{n_1!(\omega_1 - 1)!} \tag{201}$$

(cf. Eq. 169, Appendix I, writing $N = n_1 + \omega_1 - 1$).

1.2 The Bose-Einstein Distribution

The total number of distinguishable configurations in the Bose-Einstein "gas" as a whole is then given by the sum of all permissible values of

$$\tilde{\Omega} = \prod_i \frac{(n_i + \omega_i - 1)!}{n_i!(\omega_i - 1)!}$$

so long as we satisfy the restrictive conditions: $\sum_i n_i = N$ and $\sum_i n_i\epsilon_i = E$. Therefore, as before (cf. Appendix II, Eq. 179, et seq.), we satisfy ourselves by seeking for a maximum of $\ln \tilde{\Omega}$ subject to these restrictive conditions.

As in Appendix II we introduce Lagrange undetermined multipliers, effectively incorporating the restrictive conditions into the expression for $\ln \tilde{\Omega}$, so that *if the restrictive conditions are satisfied* we may write

$$\ln \tilde{\Omega} = \sum_i [\ln (n_i + \omega_i - 1)! - \ln n_i! - \ln (\omega_i - 1)!] + \alpha\left[\sum_i n_i - N\right] + \beta\left[\sum_i n_i\epsilon_i - E\right], \tag{202}$$

(cf. Eq. 189, Appendix II).
As before, we may now regard all the n_i's in Eq. 202 as independent, and of course we treat N and E as constants. Thus, for a maximum of $\ln \tilde{\Omega}$ as given by Eq. 202, we require

$$\frac{\partial \ln \tilde{\Omega}}{\partial n_i} = 0, \qquad \textbf{for all and every } \mathbf{n_i}.$$

That is, using Stirling's approximation again ($\ln n! \approx n \ln n - n$), we require

$$\ln (n_i + \omega_i - 1) - \ln n_i + \alpha + \beta\epsilon_i = 0, \qquad \text{for each and every } n_i. \tag{203}$$

Hence setting $\beta = -1/kT$, we have

$$\frac{n_i}{\omega_i} = \frac{1}{e^{(\epsilon_i/kT - \alpha)} - 1}, \tag{204a}$$

ignoring a spurious factor $(1 - 1/\omega_i)$ on the right-hand side of Eq. 204*a*, bearing in mind the basic assumption of our model, as discussed in the text, that $\omega_i \gg 1$.

If we now denote (as we have done previously) the degeneracy of a *single* energy level by g_i and its occupancy by n_i, we can then write

$$\boxed{\frac{n_i}{g_i} = \frac{1}{e^{(\epsilon_i/kT - \alpha)} - 1}}, \tag{204b}$$

(which is Eq. 94).

1.3 The Entropy

We can write down the entropy from Planck's equation $S = k \ln \Omega$, using as before $\ln \Omega_{\max}$ for $\ln \Omega$, and we find

$$S = -k \sum_i [f_i \ln f_i - (1 + f_i) \ln (1 + f_i)] g_i, \tag{205}$$

where $f_i \equiv n_i/g_i$. The first term of this expression reminds us immediately of Boltzmann's original expression for the entropy of a classical gas (cf. Section 1.2.1 and footnote on p. 6). In fact if $f_i \ll 1$, the second term in Eq. 205 becomes negligible in comparison with the first term, and indeed $f_i \ll 1$ is the condition for ensuring the validity of classical statistics.

2 QUALITATIVE COMMENTS

2.1 Physical Significance of α

The parameter α now figures explicitly in the distribution function, Eq. 204*b*, and cannot be readily eliminated; a similar situation arises when we deal with Fermi-Dirac statistics (cf. Appendix IV). We have already identified the physical significance of the parameter β ($\beta = -1/kT$), so now let us inquire about the physical significance of α. Physically, the "restrictive" condition $\sum_i n_i = N$, when applied to a gaseous model, states that not merely are we limited to N particles in the container, but moreover that these particles are quite *free* to go from state to state in the container (at least as far as this restrictive condition is concerned) with the sole requirement that the total number of particles N remains constant. In fact the requirement that the total number of elements in the assembly must remain constant embodies much of what we mean by particles or atoms in statistical mechanics.

If an assembly has not yet reached a state of equilibrium, progressive changes will still be taking place in the probable occupations numbers of the various states; i.e., n_i, n_j, etc., would be changing with time. When statistical equilibrium, with which we are concerned, is reached, then naturally n_i, n_j, etc., will have reached stationary values, and no further net transfer of particles from state to state will occur. Correspondingly, if we have *two* assemblies of similar material at the same temperature, and they are free to exchange particles with one another (such as a liquid in contact with its vapor), then if both assemblies can be characterized by the *same* α, there should be no further net transfer of particles from one assembly to the other. In thermodynamic language we would be considering two "open" systems, and in equilibrium we would say that the chemical potentials ($\mu = \alpha kT$), of the two systems are the same. Thus it turns out that for two open assemblies of the same material to be in over-all equilibrium with one another, we require that α and β should be the same for both; this means in thermodynamic language that the chemical potentials and temperatures of the two assemblies are the same (remembering that $\beta = -1/kT$). Colloquially we can say that the parameter β for an assembly (and hence its temperature) determines the "tendency to gain or lose energy," and the parameter α (and hence the chemical potential of the assembly) determines the "tendency to gain or lose particles."

2.2 Contrast with Classical Distribution

Why does α figure explicitly in the distribution function for the Bose-Einstein and Fermi-Dirac "gas," and *not* in the distribution function for the classical gas or, for that matter, for the assembly of localizable particles? We might answer this in very rough terms as follows: The very freedom of particles to go from state to state in the gaslike model suggests that the relative number of particles (n_i/N) in any *one* given state will in general be influenced by the occupation numbers of *other* states, and will depend explicitly on the over-all density of particles which have to be "fitted in" to the various states. In other words, generally in a gaslike model, we ought to *expect* that n_i/N will depend not only on the so-called Boltzmann factor ($e^{\beta\epsilon_i} = e^{-\epsilon_i/kT}$, i.e., depending directly on only that particular energy level and the temperature), but also to some degree on the distribution of particles in the *remainder* of the assembly. This is indeed the role of the parameter α, so that more generally we really ought to expect the complete factor $e^{\alpha+\beta\epsilon_i}$ to appear explicitly in the distribution function, as indeed it does with both Bose-Einstein and Fermi-Dirac statistics.

In the limiting case of the classical gas (which happens to apply adequately to all "real" gases), the density of particles is so low (implying $n_i/g_i \ll 1$ for all i) that we can say colloquially that the occupation of any particular elementary state by a particle has negligible influence on the occupation of any other state by any other particle. Thus it is not surprising that in this limit the relative number of particles occupying a state (n_i/N) can be expressed independently of other occupation numbers, or in other words that α can be readily eliminated.

In an assembly of (strictly) *localized* elements it is then also obvious why α is readily eliminated. Precisely because the elements *are* localized (and hence definitely "distinguishable"), the occupation of any particular localized state by one particular particle only affects the probability of any other particle occupying any of *its* localized states through the restrictive condition on the over-all energy. We are in effect dealing with a classical assembly *for counting purposes*, because each element is separately localized, and consequently it is very natural that we arrive at a classical expression for the occupancy numbers.

APPENDIX IV
FERMI-DIRAC STATISTICS

1 ANALYSIS

1.1 Number of Configurations

We have ω_1 particle states, and n_1 identical particles to distribute among these particle states with the stringent restriction that *at most only one particle can occupy each state.* Obviously this demands $n_1 \leq \omega_1$. Consider now this sketch for the case of $\omega_1 = 8$, $n_1 = 4$:

1 1 0 0 0 1 0 1

This represents the situation where we have eight particle states in all, of which the first, second, sixth, and eighth are occupied (by one particle each) and the remainder of the states are unoccupied. More generally we have to ask in how many distinguishable ways altogether (Ω_1) we can arrange ω_1 symbols, n_1 of which are identical with one another (the "1's"), and the remainder, $\omega_1 - n_1$ in number (the "0's"), are also indistinguishable among themselves. The problem is then once more reduced in form to that discussed in Appendix I, and we have immediately

$$\Omega_1 = \frac{\omega_1!}{n_1!(\omega_1 - n_1)!}. \tag{206}$$

1.2 The Fermi-Dirac Distribution

The total number of distinguishable configurations in the Fermi-Dirac "gas" is then given by the sum of all permissible values of

$$\tilde{\Omega} = \prod_i \frac{\omega_i!}{n_i!(\omega_i - n_i)!}, \tag{207}$$

so long as we satisfy the restrictive conditions: $\sum_i n_i = N$ and $\sum_i n_i\epsilon_i = E$. So once again we seek for a maximum of $\ln \tilde{\Omega}$ as given by Eq. 207, say $\ln \Omega_{max}$, subject to these restrictive conditions. We thus seek for a maximum of the expression

$$\ln \Omega = \sum_i [\ln \omega_i! - \ln n_i! - \ln (\omega_i - n_i)!] + \alpha\left(\sum_i n_i - N\right) + \beta\left(\sum_i n_i\epsilon_i - E\right), \quad (208)$$

where now all the n_i's are to be treated as independent, and where N and E are to be treated as constants (cf. Eq. 202, Appendix III, and Eq. 189, Appendix II). This then leads in the usual way to

$$-\ln n_i + \ln (\omega_i - n_i) + \alpha + \beta\epsilon_i = 0, \qquad \textbf{for each and every } \mathbf{n_i}. \quad (209)$$

Thus

$$\frac{\omega_i - n_i}{n_i} = e^{-(\alpha+\beta\epsilon_i)},$$

or

$$\frac{n_i}{\omega_i} = \frac{1}{e^{(\epsilon_i/kT-\alpha)} + 1}, \quad (210a)$$

if as usual we write $\beta = -1/kT$. Hence again, if we now denote the degeneracy of a *single* energy level by g_i and its occupancy by n_i, we may write

$$\boxed{\frac{n_i}{g_i} = \frac{1}{e^{(\epsilon_i/kT-\alpha)} + 1}}, \qquad \text{(which is Eq. 99).} \quad (210b)$$

1.3 The Entropy

The entropy can as usual be written down from $S = k \ln \Omega$, and using $\ln \Omega_{max}$ for $\ln \Omega$, we have

$$S = -k \sum_i [f_i \ln f_i + (1 - f_i) \ln (1 - f_i)]g_i, \quad (211)$$

where as before $f_i \equiv n_i/g_i$. We notice that the first term on the right-hand side of Eq. 211 is essentially Boltzmann's expression for the entropy of a classical gas, and once again the second term would become negligible if $f_i \ll 1$, which is indeed the appropriate limit for ensuring the validity of classical statistics. In Fermi-Dirac statistics moreover we can readily interpret in broad terms the significance of *both* terms of Eq. 211. Because of the Pauli Exclusion Principle, states must either be occupied by single particles or be empty. Equation 211 suggests that, if we wish, we might think of this problem as that of counting semiclassically an entropy contribution of the particles *and* of the "holes" (i.e., empty states).

2 COMMENTS

(1) We notice that in the distribution function for the Fermi-Dirac "gas" the parameter α figures explicitly and cannot be eliminated readily. The physical significance of α and its role are commented on at the close of Appendix III.

(2) If we wished to make a first guess at an expression for the entropy arising from the random mixture of atoms in a simple two-component alloy of relative concentrations x and $1 - x$ (the "mixing entropy"), then a similar physical argument to that following Eq. 211 suggests that we should write as a first approximation

$$S_{\text{mix}} \propto x \ln x + (1 - x) \ln (1 - x). \tag{212}$$

If the concentration of one component is very small (e.g., $x \ll 1$), then only one term is important; i.e., if $x \ll 1$

$$S_{\text{mix}} \propto x \ln x. \tag{212a}$$

APPENDIX V
"INTERMEDIATE" STATISTICS

1 ANALYSIS

1.1 Introduction

We consider now the situation (relevant to the "gaslike" model) where we have ω_1 particle states, and n_1 identical particles which may occupy any of these states with the restriction that no single state may be occupied by more than p particles. Thus specifically Fermi-Dirac statistics correspond to setting $p = 1$, whereas Bose-Einstein statistics correspond to $p \to \infty$. Intermediate situations (leading to "intermediate statistics") have been discussed by Gentile (1940, 1942) and others (e.g., Guénault and MacDonald, 1962). There is no obvious fundamental application for these intermediate statistics *in general*, but the method of analysis has the advantage of being a common approach to both Fermi-Dirac and Bose-Einstein statistics, and the general expressions for arbitrary p are of some interest (cf. again Guénault and MacDonald, 1962).

1.2 Number of Configurations

Let us assume $\omega_1 = 8$, $n_1 = 11$, and $p = 3$, and now consider the sketch.

2 0 3 1 2 0 0 3

The sketch represents the situation where there are eight particle states; the second, sixth, and seventh states are unoccupied, the fourth is occupied by a single particle, the first and fifth are occupied by two particles, and the third and eighth by three particles; thus in all there are eleven particles in the various states. More generally we consider the situation where there are ω_1 particle states, $n_1^{(0)}$ "zeros" (all indistinguishable from one another), $n_1^{(1)}$ "ones" (indistinguishable from one another), $n_1^{(2)}$ "twos," . . . , $n_1^{(p)}$ "p's." Thus the total number of distinguishable configurations is given by

$$\Omega_1 = \frac{\omega_1!}{n_1^{(0)}!\, n_1^{(1)}!\, n_1^{(2)}! \cdots n_1^{(p)}!}, \tag{213}$$

together with the condition that

$$\sum_r n_1^{(r)} = \omega_1, \tag{214}$$

i.e., that the total number of symbols, 0, 1, 2, . . . , p used to express *occupancy* of the states must of course equal the total number of states.

1.3 The Distribution Function

The over-all *total* number of distinguishable arrangements for the "gas" will thus be given by the sum of all permissible values of

$$\tilde{\Omega} = \prod_i \frac{\omega_i!}{n_i^{(0)}!\, n_i^{(1)}!\, n_i^{(2)}! \cdots n_i^{(p)}!}, \tag{215}$$

subject to the familiar restrictive conditions on the total number of particles N and the total energy E; these conditions now read

$$\sum_{i,r} r n_i^{(r)} = N,$$

$$\sum_{i,r} \epsilon_i r n_i^{(r)} = E,$$

as well as the set of conditions from Eq. 214

$$\sum_r n_i^{(r)} = \omega_i, \qquad \textit{for each index } i. \tag{214a}$$

Once again we satisfy ourselves by seeking a maximum of $\ln \tilde{\Omega}$ subject to these conditions, and this leads us finally to

$$-\ln n_i^{(r)} + \gamma_i + \alpha r + \beta r \epsilon_i = 0, \qquad \textbf{for each and every r and i.} \tag{216a}$$

Thus

$$n_i^{(r)} = e^{\gamma_i} e^{r(\alpha + \beta \epsilon_i)}. \tag{216b}$$

Substituting this solution in Eq. 214*a*, we find

$$e^{\gamma_i} = \omega_i \sum_{r=0}^{p} e^{r(\alpha+\beta\epsilon_i)}$$

and hence

$$\frac{n_i^{(r)}}{\omega_i} = \frac{e^{r(\alpha+\beta\epsilon_i)}}{\sum_{r=0}^{p} e^{r(\alpha+\beta\epsilon_i)}} \tag{216c}$$

Now the total occupancy of the ω_i states, say n_i, is given by

$$n_i = \sum_{r=1}^{p} r n_i^{(r)};$$

therefore

$$\frac{n_i}{\omega_i} = \frac{\sum_{r=1}^{p} r e^{r(\alpha+\beta\epsilon_i)}}{\sum_{r=0}^{p} e^{r(\alpha+\beta\epsilon_i)}} \tag{216d}$$

Consequently, if as usual we now write n_i for the probable occupancy of a *single* energy level and g_i for the degeneracy of that level, we have finally

$$\frac{n_i}{g_i} = \frac{\sum_{r=1}^{p} r e^{r(\alpha+\beta\epsilon_i)}}{\sum_{r=0}^{p} e^{r(\alpha+\beta\epsilon_i)}}$$

Therefore

$$\boxed{\frac{n_i}{g_i} = \frac{1}{e^{-(\alpha+\beta\epsilon_i)} - 1} - \frac{p+1}{e^{-(p+1)(\alpha+\beta\epsilon_i)} - 1}}, \tag{217}$$

and as always $\beta = -1/kT$.

If now in Eq. 217, $p = 0$, then $n_i/g_i \equiv 0$, as we should naturally expect!

If

$$p = 1, \qquad \frac{n_i}{g_i} = \frac{1}{e^{(\epsilon_i/kT-\alpha)} + 1}, \tag{218}$$

i.e., the distribution function already derived in Appendix IV for Fermi-Dirac statistics.

Finally if

$$p \to \infty, \quad \text{then} \quad \frac{n_i}{g_i} = \frac{1}{e^{(\epsilon_i/kT-\alpha)} - 1}, \tag{219}^*$$

i.e., the distribution function already derived in Appendix III for Bose-Einstein statistics.

2 COMMENTS

Equation 216*b* is also of some interest in its own right. We have obviously

$$\frac{n_i^{(r)}}{n_i^{(s)}} = e^{(r-s)(\alpha+\beta\epsilon_i)}. \tag{220}$$

It seems worth noting that this is a *completely general* expression valid for any value of p (and hence of course valid in particular for Bose-Einstein statistics, for Fermi-Dirac statistics, and, as we shall see, for the "classical" limit if we interpret Eq. 220 suitably).

2.1 Pauli Exclusion Principle

If the Pauli Principle applies, then in Eq. 220 we have only to consider $s = 0$ and $r = 1$, i.e.,

$$\frac{n_i^{(1)}}{n_i^{(0)}} = e^{\alpha+\beta\epsilon_i}. \tag{221}$$

Now any elementary state must either be occupied or vacant, and so obviously

$$n_i^{(0)} + n_i^{(1)} = g_i;$$

hence, if we now write here $n_i^{(1)} = n_i$, we have

$$\frac{n_i}{g_i - n_i} = e^{\alpha+\beta\epsilon_i}, \tag{222a}$$

i.e.,

$$\frac{n_i}{g_i} = \frac{1}{e^{-(\alpha+\beta\epsilon_i)} + 1}, \tag{222b}$$

* This result for $p \to \infty$ follows from Eq. 217 so long as $e^{(\epsilon_i/kT-\alpha)} > 1$ for all $\epsilon_i \geq 0$, i.e., if α (which determines the chemical potential) is always ≤ 0 for $p \to \infty$. Moreover, this is also an obviously necessary requirement to ensure that all occupation numbers n_i in Eq. 219 are positive.

giving us again directly the distribution function for Fermi-Dirac statistics.

2.2 The Classical Limit

The classical limit emerges when the occupancy numbers are so low that only single occupancy of any level (i.e., $n_i^{(1)}$) is at all significant, and also moreover $n_i^{(1)} \ll n_i^{(0)}$. Hence immediately from Eq. 222*a* we have

$$\frac{n_i}{g_i} = e^{\alpha + \beta\epsilon_i}, \qquad (223)^*$$

in the classical limit.

* This expression, which we can now also write in the familiar form

$$\frac{n_i}{N} = \frac{g_i e^{-\epsilon_i/kT}}{\sum_i g_i e^{-\epsilon_i/kT}}, \qquad (223a)$$

is valid, as we have seen, both for an assembly of localized elements quite generally and for nonlocalizable elements *in the classical limit.* The reason, mentioned also in Appendix III, is essentially that in both these cases we can analyze the situation *as if* the elements (or "atoms") were always distinguishable. In the localizable case the elements *are* indeed distinguishable precisely because they occupy different sites in space (although not necessarily "real" space), whereas in the "gaseous" case in the classical limit the density of particles is so low that the chance of multiple occupancy of any level is quite negligible.

REFERENCES

(Pages on which author is cited are given in brackets; the number immediately following a reference to a Fig. or a Table gives the page on which that Figure or Table will be found.)

Alkemade, C. T. J., N. G. van Kampen, and D. K. C. MacDonald, 1963, *Proc. Roy. Soc. (London), A*, In press. [135]

Barron, T. H. K., 1956, *Nature,* **178,** 871. [127]

Barron, T. H. K., 1957, Annals of Physics, **1,** 77. [58; 127]

Beattie, J. A., 1926, *J. Math. and Phys.*, **6,** 1. [Table 2, p. 56]

Bernal, J. D., 1959, *Nature,* **183,** 141. [66]

Blackman, M., 1941, *Reports on Progress in Physics, (Phys. Soc. London)*, **8,** 11. [46]

Blackman, M., 1942, *Proc. Phys. Soc. (London)*, **54,** 377. [48]

Boltzmann, L., 1872, *Wien. Ber.*, **66,** 275. [6]

Born, M., 1949a, *Ann. de l'Inst. H. Poincaré,* **11,** 1 (cf. also Born, 1949b). [11]

Born, M., 1949b, *Natural Philosophy of Cause and Chance,* Clarendon Press, Oxford. [19]

Born, M., and M. Göppert-Mayer, 1933, *Handbuch der Physik* (Springer, Berlin), **24**(2), 676. [126]

Born, M., and Th. v. Kármán, 1912, 1913, *Phys. Z.*, **13,** 297; **14,** 15. [46]

Brillouin, L., 1946, *Wave Propagation in Periodic Structures,* McGraw-Hill, New York, 1st Ed., 1946, 2nd Ed., 1953. [46; 53]

Broda, E., 1955, *Ludwig Boltzmann,* F. Deuticke, Vienna. [4]

Brussels Conference, 1956, *Proc. of the Int. Symposium on Transport Processes in Stat. Mech.*, Brussels, August 1956, edited by I. Prigogine, Interscience Publishers, New York, London (published 1958). [132]

Chandrasekhar, S., 1943, *Rev. Mod. Phys.*, **15,** 1. [131; 132]

Daunt, J. G., 1962, *Physics Today (Am. Phys. Soc.)*, **15,** 26. [108]

Debye, P., 1912, *Ann. Phys. (Lpz.)*, **35,** 789. [46; Fig. 9, p. 52]

de Groot, S. R., 1951, *Thermodynamics of Irreversible Processes,* North-Holland Publishing Co., Amsterdam. [1]

de Klerk, D., M. J. Steenland, and C. J. Gorter, 1949, *Physica*, **15**, 649. [Fig. 2*a*, p. 16]
Drude, P., 1900, *Ann. Phys., Lpz.*, **1**, 566; **3**, 369. [88]
Dugdale, J. S., and D. K. C. MacDonald, 1954, *Phys. Rev.*, **96**, 57. [125; 126]
Einstein, A., 1907, *Ann. Phys., Lpz.*, **22**, 180, 800. [39; Fig. 7, p. 44]
Einstein, A., 1911, *Ann. Phys., Lpz.*, **34**, 170; **35**, 679. [39]
Feynman, R. P., 1955, "Application of Quantum Mechanics to Liquid Helium," *Progress in Low Temperature Physics*, edited by Gorter; Vol. 1, pp. 17–53, North-Holland Press. [107]
Feynman, R. P., 1957, *Rev. Mod. Phys.*, **29**, 205. [107]
Fowler, R. H., 1936, *Statistical Mechanics*, 2nd Ed., Cambridge University Press. [Preface; 19]
Fowler, R. H., and E. A. Guggenheim, 1939, *Statistical Thermodynamics*, Cambridge University Press. [Preface; Table 2, p. 56]
Gardner, W. E., and N. Kürti, 1954, *Proc. Roy. Soc.* (*London*), *A*, **223**, 542. [Fig. 6*b*, p. 34]
Gentile, G., 1940, 1942, *Nuovo Cimento*, **17**, 493; **19**, 106. [157]
Guénault, A. M., and D. K. C. MacDonald, 1962, *Molecular Physics* (*London*), **5**, 525 [105; 157]
Hill, R. W., and P. L. Smith, 1953, *Proc. Phys. Soc.* (*London*), *A*, **66**, 228. [Fig. 6*a*, p. 33]
Kürti, N., P. Lainé, and F. E. Simon, 1937, *Compt. rend.* (*Paris*), **204**, 754. [Fig. 2*b*, p. 16]
Kürti, N., and F. E. Simon, 1949, *Proc. Int. Conf. Low Temperatures*, Massachusetts Institute of Technology. [Fig. 2*b*, p. 16]
London, F., 1938, *Phys. Rev.*, **54**, 947. [9; 70; 102; 103; Fig. 17, p. 104; 105]
MacDonald, D. K. C., 1952, *Prog. in Met. Phys.*, **3**, 42. [48]
MacDonald, D. K. C., 1961, *Phil. Mag.*, **6**, 1407. [135]
MacDonald, D. K. C., 1962, *Noise and Fluctuations: An Introduction*, John Wiley and Sons, New York. [19; 133; 135]
MacDonald, D. K. C., and W. B. Pearson, 1953, *Proc. Roy. Soc.* (*London*), *A*, **219**, 373. [Table 4, p. 64]
MacDonald, D. K. C., and S. K. Roy, 1955, *Phys. Rev.*, **97**, 673. [126]
McDougall, J., and E. C. Stoner, 1938, *Phil. Trans. Roy. Soc.* (*London*), *A*, **237**, 67. [91]
Mendelssohn, K., 1956, *Handbuch der Physik* (Springer, Berlin), **15**, 370. [106; Fig. 18, p. 106]
Mott, N. F., 1934, *Proc. Roy. Soc.* (*London*), *A*, **146**, 465. [65]
Mott, N. F., and H. Jones, 1936, *The Theory of the Properties of Metals and Alloys*, Clarendon Press, Oxford. [Table 3, p. 61; Table 4, p. 64; 65; Table 5, p. 66; 68; 93]
Nernst, W., and F. A. Lindemann, 1911, *S. B. preuss. Akad. Wiss.*, **22**, 494. [45]
Onsager, L., 1931, *Phys. Rev.*, **37**, 405; **38**, 2265. [1]
Planck, M., 1932, *The Theory of Heat* (Translation by H. L. Brose), Macmillan, London. [7]

Prigogine, I., 1947, *Etude thermodynamique des phénomènes irreversibles*, Dunod, Paris. [1]

Raman, C. V., 1941, *Proc. Indian Acad. Sci.*, *A*, **14**, 459. [48]

Rushbrooke, G. S., 1949, *Introduction to Statistical Mechanics*, Clarendon Press, Oxford. [Preface; 9; 40; 75]

Schottky, W., 1921, 1922, *Phys. Zs.*, **22**, 1; **23**, 9, 448. [27; 29]

Simon, F. E., 1924, *Zeits.*, *f. Phys.*, **27**, 157. [65]

Stein, Gertrude, 1922, "Sacred Emily," from *Geography and Plays*, Four Seas Co., Boston. [70]

Ter Haar, D., 1954, *Elements of Statistical Mechanics*, Rinehart and Co., New York. [4]

Thomson, William (Lord Kelvin), 1854, *Trans. Roy. Soc. Edinburgh*, **21**, Part 1. [3]

Tolman, R. C., 1938, *The Principles of Statistical Mechanics*, Clarendon Press, Oxford. [Preface]

Walker, C. B., 1956, *Phys. Rev.*, **103**, 547. [Fig. 8*b*, p. 51]

Waterston, J. J., 1846, *Proc. Roy. Soc.* (*London*), **5**, 604; 1892, *Phil. Trans. Roy. Soc.* (*London*), *A* **183**, 1. [5]

Wilson, A. H., 1953, *The Theory of Metals*, 2nd Ed., Cambridge University Press. [68; 91; 93]

Wu, T. Y., and D. Rivier, 1961, *Helv. Phys. Acta.*, **34**, 661. [11]

Zemansky, M., 1943, *Heat and Thermodynamics*, 2nd ed., McGraw-Hill, New York. [24; 73]

Ziman, J. M., 1960, *Electrons and Phonons*, Clarendon Press, Oxford. [68]

A GLOSSARY OF SYMBOLS WITH THEIR SIGNIFICANCE

Symbol		Page No.*
B	Bulk modulus.	24
C; $\tilde{C}$	Interaction constants (proportional to one another) (determining the scattering of electrons).	62
C_V; C_p	Differential specific heats at constant volume (V) and at constant pressure (p), usually per mole.	4
c_V; c_p	Specific heats *per unit volume.*	60
$d\tilde{n}$	Probable number of photons per unit volume in frequency interval $d\nu$.	113
$\mathbf{dx}$	Denotes $dx\, dy\, dz$.	120
$\mathbf{dp}$	Denotes $dp_x\, dp_y\, dp_z$.	120
$\mathbf{dv}$	Denotes $dv_x\, dv_y\, dv_z$.	120
E	The energy (or so-called internal energy in thermodynamics) of an assembly of elements. The same symbol is used when we deal with one mole, but it is then always specified that one mole is involved.	2
$\tilde{E}$	Energy per unit volume of electromagnetic radiation.	110
$\tilde{E}_\nu$	Energy per unit volume of electromagnetic radiation in frequency interval $d\nu$.	110

*The page number quoted gives either the first, or a typical, page where the symbol is employed.

Symbol		Page No.
E	Electric field vector.	109
f_i	"Distribution function" defined by: $f_i = n_i/g_i$.	83
$\mathcal{f}_0$	Fraction of particles in ground state in Bose-Einstein assembly below T_c, the condensation temperature.	102
F	Helmholtz free energy of an assembly ($F = E - TS$). The same symbol is used when we deal with one mole, but it is then always specified that one mole is involved.	23
$\mathfrak{F}(t)$	Total force acting on Brownian particle as a function of time t.	133
$F(t)$	Very rapidly fluctuating part of force acting on Brownian particle, as function of time t.	134
g; g_i	The degeneracy of a particular elementary state (the subscript i would refer to a state of energy ϵ_i).	15
$g(\epsilon)$	Number of elementary particle-states per unit energy interval in gaslike models.	90
$g_1(\epsilon)$	Number of elementary states per unit volume per unit energy interval in gaslike model (known as the density of states).	90
H	Magnetic field.	34
H; $\bar{H}$	Used (but in Section 1.2.1 only) to denote integral expressions occurring in Boltzmann's "H-theorem."	6
H	Magnetic field vector.	109
$\mathfrak{I}$	Intensity of electromagnetic radiation.	111
$\mathfrak{k}$	Constant relating entropy to natural logarithm of total number of complexions; and more specifically identified as:	8
k	Boltzmann's constant (1.4×10^{-16} erg/deg. $= 1.4 \times 10^{-23}$ joule/deg.).	8
k	Wave vector (with components $[2\pi\mathfrak{n}_1/L, 2\pi\mathfrak{n}_2/L, 2\pi\mathfrak{n}_3/L]$).	46
$\mathfrak{L}$	Loss per second by radiation of electromagnetic energy.	111
$\mathfrak{m}$	The magnetic moment appropriate to a single element (e.g., a paramagnetic molecule).	18
$\mathfrak{M}$	The total magnetic moment of an assembly of elements.	18

Symbol		Page No.
m	The mass of an element or particle.	62
M	Molar mass.	63
$\mathfrak{n}_1$, $\mathfrak{n}_2$, and $\mathfrak{n}_3$	Integers determining components of the wave vector **k**.	48
$\mathfrak{n}$	Wave number defined by $\mathfrak{n} = (\mathfrak{n}_1^2 + \mathfrak{n}_2^2 + \mathfrak{n}_3^2)^{1/2}$.	48
$\tilde{\mathfrak{n}}$	The maximum value of $\mathfrak{n}$.	86
n_i	The "internal distribution"; i.e., the probable number of elements occupying elementary states of energy ϵ_i in an assembly.	71
$n_i^{(r)}$	A "(partial) internal distribution"; viz., the probable number of the elementary states of energy ϵ_i which are occupied by exactly r particles. $\left(\text{Hence: } n_i = \sum_r r n_i^{(r)}\right)$.	158
N	The number of elements (e.g., particles, atoms, molecules) in an assembly. The number N is always assumed to be very large.	4
N_1	Number of elements or particles per unit volume in assembly.	36, 86
$\tilde{N}$	Number of atoms per unit volume (in connection with lattice vibration analysis).	50
$\mathfrak{N}$	Avogadro's number ($\sim 6 \times 10^{23}$ per mole). We have the relation $\mathfrak{N}k = R$, where k is Boltzmann's constant, and R is the gas constant ($R \approx 8.3$ joules/deg. mole, or about 2 cal/deg. mole).	11
N	Number of normal modes of vibration.	49
$\tilde{\mathsf{N}}$	Number of normal modes of vibration per unit volume of assembly or "container."	49
P	The relative probability that some selected macroscopically defined state of an assembly may be expected to occur spontaneously ($P = \omega/\Omega$, or $P = \tilde{\omega}/\Omega$).	18
p	Pressure.	2
$\mathbf{p}$	Momentum vector with components $[p_x, p_y, p_z]$.	120
$\mathbf{r}$	The vector with components $[x, y, z]$.	48
R	The gas constant appearing in the ideal gas equation: $-\ p\mathcal{V} = RT$ (for 1 mole); R is	11

Symbol		Page No.
	related to Avogadro's number through Boltzmann's constant, namely: $R = \mathfrak{N}k$.	
S	The entropy of an assembly. The same symbol is used when we deal with one mole, but it is then always specified that one mole is involved.	6
$\mathcal{S}$	Thermoelectric power.	3
T	Absolute temperature.	80
$\mathbf{v}$	Velocity vector with components $[v_x, v_y, v_z]$.	120
V	The volume within which an assembly of elements is contained.	3
$V(x)$	Occurs occasionally (e.g., Section 2.1) for the potential energy of an element or particle corresponding to a displacement x.	37
$\mathcal{V}$	The molar volume; i.e., the volume which would be occupied by $\mathfrak{N}$ elements.	13
x, y, z	Cartesian coordinates to determine position of an element.	37
$\tilde{z}$	The height of the isothermal equilibrium atmosphere at which the density ρ is such that $\rho(\tilde{z}) = \rho_0 e^{-1}$.	123
Z	Symbol for the "partition function" (per element or per oscillator). Thus in an assembly of independent localizable elements: $Z = \sum_i g_i \exp(-\epsilon_i/kT)$.	26
α	Lagrange undetermined multiplier relating to number of elements or particles in an assembly.	80
β	(i) Coefficient of thermal expansion.	60
β	(ii) Lagrange undetermined multiplier relating to temperature ($\beta = -1/kT$).	80
γ	The Grüneisen anharmonicity parameter. If the solid has a characteristic temperature θ and volume V, this parameter is defined by: $\gamma \equiv -(d \ln \theta / d \ln V)$.	59
ϵ; ϵ_i	Energy (states) of individual elements, particles, atoms or molecules. It is the underlying assumption of an assembly of independent elements that individual, or "pri-	12

Symbol		Page No.
	vate," energy states can in fact be ascribed to single elements or particles.	
$\tilde{\epsilon}$	A maximum particle energy mentioned in the analysis of Fermi-Dirac statistics.	85
ζ	Conventionally used to denote chemical potential (per particle) (i.e., "Fermi energy") in Fermi-Dirac statistics.	84
θ	A characteristic temperature related to some appropriate characteristic frequency ν by $k\theta = h\nu$. Particular models lead to: θ_E, the Einstein characteristic temperature; θ_D, the Debye characteristic temperature; and: θ_S, the Schottky characteristic temperature.	53
λ	Algebraic coefficient referring to anharmonic (cubic) potential energy term.	124
μ	Chemical potential (per particle) of an assembly; ($\mu = \alpha kT$).	80
ν	Frequency.	48
ξ	Alternative choice of coordinates to describe particle displacements when analyzing normal modes of vibration.	37
Π	The Peltier heat at the junction of two conductors.	3
$\prod_i$	Denoting a product of similar factors characterized by the index i.	72
ρ	(i) Electrical resistivity.	62
$\rho(z)$	(ii) Used in Section 4.3 to denote density at height z of isothermal atmosphere.	123
χ_H	Magnetic susceptibility.	35
χ_T	Isothermal compressibility.	60
χ_S	Adiabatic (isentropic) compressibility.	60
ψ	Wave function for single particle appropriate to a model involving independent elements.	76
Ψ	To denote wave function of an assembly of particles.	83
ω	(i) (Angular) Frequency, i.e., $\omega = 2\pi\nu$.	48
ω; $\bar{\omega}$	(ii) The number of distinguishable "microscopic" complexions corresponding to some	17, 139

Symbol		Page No.
	selected macroscopically defined state, or range of states, of an assembly.	
ω_i; ω_j	Number of distinct elementary states in the *i*th and *j*th groups of energy levels in the analysis of the gaslike model.	71
Ω	Total number of distinguishable "microscopic" configurations, or "complexions," of an assembly.	6
$\tilde{\Omega}$	The number of complexions for a whole assembly corresponding to some particular choice of internal distribution for the individual particles. Thus for the gaslike assembly: $\tilde{\Omega} = \prod_i \Omega_i$.	141
Ω_i; Ω_j	The number of distinguishable configurations in the *i*th (and *j*th) groups or "subassemblies" of particles in the gaslike model.	72
Ω_{max}	The maximum value for $\tilde{\Omega}$, subject to the usual restrictive conditions; $\ln \Omega_{max}$ for an assembly is then in general a very adequate approximation for $\ln \Omega$.	141
< >	The average value of a quantity. Thus in classical statistical mechanics, if ϵ is the energy of a (one-dimensional) simple harmonic oscillator, then: $<\epsilon> = kT$.	62

INDEX

(1) Where a chapter or appendix is referred to, this means that the item concerned is a major topic in that chapter; the page number immediately following gives the *opening* page of the chapter or appendix concerned.

(2) Certain words (e.g., "Entropy") are marked with an asterisk. These are subjects which occur frequently in the book; generally speaking, the page references are therefore not exhaustive for these words.